The Winter at Valley Forge

THE WINTER
AT
VALLEY FORGE

— ★ —

by F. VAN WYCK MASON

Illustrated by HARPER JOHNSON

RANDOM HOUSE · NEW YORK

To my most amusing young neighbor

J. COOPER GRAHAME III

in the hope that he and others
of his generation
may derive some inspiration from this tale.

Contents

Foreword

To those of my readers who may wonder how exactly I have stuck to facts and incidences in The Winter at Valley Forge, I wish to say that the only fictional characters are Gil Weston, Silver Hawk, Corporal Cassidy, and Farmer Matson, who represents a family well known in those parts. All units and their officers are authentic.

The incident of "Paddy," and the attack on the farmhouse which is described at the end of the story, were historical incidents and all the events depicted as taking place in the encampment are typical of that dreadful winter.

F. VAN WYCK MASON

GUNNERS' HILL,

RIDERWOOD, MARYLAND.

The Winter at Valley Forge

1
The Black Autumn

VALLEY FORGE—OUR NATION HAS NO PROUDER chapter in her history than the one written during the winter of 1777 and 1778. That was when George Washington led about ten thousand troops into winter quarters at that place on the Schuyl-kill River, in Pennsylvania, about twenty miles northwest of Philadelphia.

It was a ragtag and bobtail army that went into Valley Forge. It had suffered many de-

3

feats and realized few victories. It was despised by the British who called it "a rabble in arms." It was an army that fought among itself and was led by generals who were jealous of each other. Some of these men even plotted against George Washington himself. The army had few weapons, not enough powder, almost no discipline. There was a serious lack of meat and flour, shoes and blankets, medicine and muskets.

In Philadelphia, the captured capital of our newborn nation, the British General, Sir William Howe, had everything Washington did not have. He had a well-trained, well-equipped, well-supplied army of Redcoats that had beaten the Americans nearly every time the two forces had met.

Howe spent that bitter winter of 1777 and 1778 in comfort. His "Lobsterbacks" and Hessians left no bloody tracks in that winter's snow. Their feet were protected by stout boots. Howe's men did not eat "firecakes" of coarse flour and water nor did they shiver in rude huts with dirt floors.

They ate red beef and juicy pork, and their winter quarters were warm.

"Let the Rebels starve and freeze this winter," said "Dandy Sir Billy" Howe, as he was called. "In the spring we'll waste no time taking care of

5

the ones who are left—if that brigand, Washington, has any men left at all."

But in the spring of '78, out of Valley Forge marched a new army. It was an army that had come through one of the cruelest winters in our country's history. More than that, it was an army that had found itself. During the dark days of snow and cold, starvation and pestilence, the Americans had learned many a priceless lesson.

What a miracle was wrought at Valley Forge! This winter encampment with its pain and suffering, its heartaches and despair, might well be called the turning point of the Revolution. The scales had tipped heavily against the cause of Independence before Valley Forge. During the six long months of Valley Forge those scales threatened to decide in final favor of a British victory.

But sometime during that terrible half-year, the scales started to swing the other way, toward the bright realization of American Independence. This change came during a time of cold that killed and sickness that stripped Washington's Army of its men. It was a time of starvation so gnawing that once when some soldiers found a cask of rotten herring they gulped down the mess in what they called "a feast."

Gaunt, shivering men stumbled into Valley Forge that December day in 1777. Their feet were wrapped in rags. Their pockets were empty because they had not been paid in weeks or months. There they straggled, the New Englanders, the New Yorkers, the New Jerseyites, the Pennsylvanians, the Marylanders and Delawarians, the Virginians and Carolinians. It did not seem that there was any hope for their cause. "Dandy Sir Billy" Howe told King George the Third that the end of the Revolution was near. As the blizzards howled, the ice thickened, the Americans' supplies failed, Howe waited for Washington's surrender. And waited and waited and waited.

Came the spring, and the British knew they had been wrong. Washington had not surrendered.

His army had not mutinied. It had not deserted in a body. Instead, the Americans had found new courage, new resolve, new faith in their cause, during that terrible winter.

The great Revolutionary writer, Thomas Paine, aide-de-camp to General Nathaniel Greene, Washington's right-hand man, said: "These are the times that try men's souls." There at Valley Forge the souls, the hearts, of the Patriots were tried, tested. They were found to be of the brave stuff that never can be conquered, no matter what the odds.

2

The Ragtags Retreat

VALLEY FORGE TOOK PLACE DURING THE WINTER months of 1777 and 1778, but the beginning of the story goes as far back as July of '77.

That was when the British General, Sir William Howe, left New York with all his troops. Howe sailed in a fleet of 260 ships with his brother, Admiral Richard Howe, commanding the armada. The British sailed down the Atlantic Coast, around Cape Charles, and up the Chesa-

9

peake Bay to a landing place on the Elk River at what is now Elkton, Maryland.

General Howe was aiming to capture Philadelphia. His plan was to attack from the head of the Chesapeake Bay instead of pressing down overland from New York. The whole idea had been given him by one of George Washington's own generals. This man bore one of the proudest names in America, but because he was a traitor he will not be named in this story. It is enough to say that while he was a prisoner of the British this man who hated Washington gave Howe a detailed plan of action. This plan, he guaranteed, would bring about the British capture of Philadelphia without the risk of a long, costly overland campaign.

Howe and his troops landed at Elkton on August 25, 1777, and moved northward toward Wilmington and Philadelphia. He met with little resistance. Washington was busy setting up a defense line on the best ground he could find. The American Commander-in-Chief set up his defenses

on Brandywine Creek, a stream flowing into the Delaware River a few miles from Wilmington.

It must be remembered in all accounts of the fighting which took place before Valley Forge that George Washington was handicapped by a lack of decent military intelligence. That is, he had too few scouts and spies, and such as he had usually were careless or stupid. Most times, Washington practically had to guess where the enemy was. Then he had to guess what direction the British were taking and what Howe intended to do once he got there.

The British, on the other hand, had excellent information. Howe had his dragoons to scout the territory ahead of him and on his flanks. He had plenty of spies, both attached to his army and among British sympathizers, the Tories. Most important of all, Howe's men knew what to report and the importance of getting those reports to him at top speed.

When Washington set up his battle line along Brandywine Creek, he covered the main fords on the approaches to Philadelphia, digging in about eleven miles northwest of Wilmington. Then he had to worry about Howe moving around him and crossing the creek at fords up or downstream. To guard against this, the American Commander-in-Chief sent out scouts to watch these unguarded fords and warn him if the British tried an end-around play. Then he put his army behind strong entrenchments on the far bank of the creek and waited for Howe to join battle.

Before the British reached Brandywine Howe

met his first American opposition of the campaign at Cooch's Bridge, near Newark, Delaware. The fight took place on September 3 when a detachment of Delaware militiamen, who called themselves "The Blue Hen's Chickens," (because their mascot was a gamecock) met the British advance guard.

The Delaware men were armed mostly with epontoons, which were homemade weapons consisting of a spear or knife lashed to a long pole. They were no match for the British troops who had muskets, of course. The fight was hardly more than a skirmish and "The Blue Hen's Chickens" had to retreat. While it was not an important battle, this was the first time in history that the Stars and Stripes, which had just been adopted as the national flag, was flown over American troops under fire.

Howe's Army, huge for those days, was slowed by its wagon trains. It took the British until September 11 to reach Brandywine Creek and meet the main American force. At the start, the British General was confident that he could roll back the ragtag, disorganized force that barred his way to Philadelphia. But after the first rounds of crashing cannon and rattling musket fire, he saw that Washington had chosen his position well. Howe realized that this victory was going to be no easy thing.

"Dandy Sir Billy" watched his Redcoats mowed down and hurled back in their first assault. He then drew off for a conference with his ranking aide, Baron Wilhelm Knypenhausen, commander of Howe's German division. These were the Hessians who made up a big part of the British Army. The American soldiers sent up a cheer when they saw the "Lobsterbacks" draw off, but neither Washington nor his generals did any cheering. They knew the British had been stung but not beaten. They also knew that Howe, in spite of his dandy's ways, was one of England's best generals with more tricks up his sleeve than a roving juggler.

"I think," the British commander was telling Baron Knypenhausen, "that these Rebels are so hungry for a victory they will not raise their eyes from what seems to be a full plate."

When the conference was over, Baron Knypenhausen threw his troops at Washington's lines again. Again the Hessians were beaten back. A third attack failed to carry the creek. The Hessians drew off to let their artillery go to work on the American entrenchments.

George Washington and his generals were uneasy. It was true that the Hessians were putting up a stiff fight, but something seemed wrong. It was as if their movements were only part of a bigger plan. Was Knypenhausen merely keeping the American front busy while Howe and his other divisions were moving to cross the Brandywine somewhere else? Washington had to know.

"General Wayne," the Commander-in-Chief snapped to his trusted and most daring aide, "Mad Anthony" Wayne, "take a force to General Sullivan's troops on our right. Reinforce him against any flanking attacks."

"Mad Anthony" welcomed the order as he welcomed any command that might put him in the thick of the fighting. He moved his men out on the double-quick, intending to support General

John Sullivan and his New Hampshire troops on the American right.

He found General Sullivan caught in a tangle of confusion. General Sullivan had received reports that Howe, with the main body of the British Army, was moving to cross the upper fords of the Brandywine fourteen miles north of the battle that was going on. In the next breath, General Sullivan was told that the first reports were wrong. He stewed in his doubt. He did not know whether he should bend his wing inward to guard against an encircling move or keep it up on the Brandywine line.

Then it seemed that his problem was solved for him. A man wearing the uniform of a major of the New Jersey Militia rode up to Sullivan.

"Reporting from the upper fords, General," the rider said, saluting. "No British in sight there."

So General Sullivan stayed where he was—and the Battle of Brandywine was lost to Washington.

After his conference with Baron Knypenhausen, General Howe had split up his force. He had left the Germans to keep up a brisk fire at the American front, but the Baron was ordered to make no attempt to carry the creek. Then Howe drove his troops hard upstream to cross the fords that were not defended. Once across, the British circled back and came downstream behind Washington's right. The first that General Sullivan knew of his danger was when the Redcoat guns roared out in blasting volleys from the rear, shredding the American line.

Who was the "New Jersey Major"? Was he a traitor, a spy or a fool who actually had not seen Howe's thousands? No one ever found out. But if he was one of Howe's men masquerading as a New Jersey militiaman, the British General must have rewarded him well. It was the false report he gave General Sullivan that won the day for the Redcoats.

Washington was under attack now from the

right-rear and the front. He knew he had lost the battle. Now the question was how to withdraw his troops without losing his army. He did not have long to ponder this question. About him his men were dropping like leaves in a windstorm. Later it was discovered that a British dragoon had drawn a sure bead on Washington himself and had held his fire for reasons he could never explain. Washington's generals were clamoring for orders.

19

He could try to save the capital, Philadelphia. But if he did, more important things, from a military point of view, would be lost. The Continental Army's main stores of munitions and supplies were at Warwick and Coventry, thirty-odd miles away, north of Chadd's Ford. These bases could not be sacrificed to try to protect Philadelphia. The capture of the capital would be a feather in Howe's cap, but the city meant practically nothing strategically.

Washington gave his orders and the Americans began a slow retreat to the north. They fought every step of the way. Howe pressed them hard, but the Americans refused to break into a rout. They carried on a bitter rear guard action that cost the British dearly. Brandywine is listed as a British victory, but Howe knew the price he was paying was a high one. He was glad to break off the fight when night fell.

The day had dealt heavily with Washington. He had lost 300 killed, 600 wounded, including the young Marquis de Lafayette, and 400 men taken prisoner. He also had lost ten precious cannon captured by the Redcoats.

Howe's forces had lost about 500 men, killed and wounded. But more important to the Americans was the fact that his army was exhausted. Howe's divisions had made a 28-mile forced march to the upper fords and back. Knypenhausen's men had been under constant fire for hours on end. Both British units were too weary to capitalize on Washington's desperate position. The Americans were able to make their withdrawal in good order while the British were forced to halt and rest.

If Howe had been able to follow up his victory at Brandywine immediately, the Revolution might well have been ended there.

3
Reeling Back

FIVE DAYS AFTER BRANDYWINE, THE BRITISH caught up with Washington again at Valley Hill near White Horse. Howe had spent those five days ranging through the Schuylkill River Valley, foraging and burning what he did not seize. Now he was ready to fight again, and there followed what some historians have called "The Battle of the Clouds."

Washington's army was still unprepared for bat-

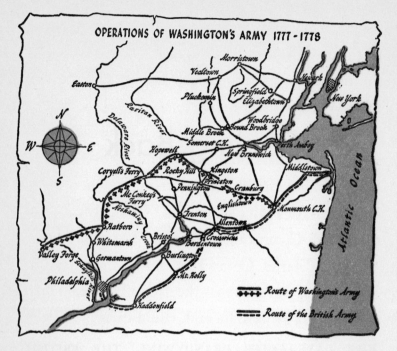

OPERATIONS OF WASHINGTON'S ARMY 1777 - 1778

┿┿┿┿ *Route of Washington's Army*
════ *Route of the British Army*

tle. The Americans were still groggy from the beating they had suffered at Brandywine. Furthermore, they were tired from the forced marches that had let them escape from that ill-fated battleground. Supplies had failed to arrive from Warren or Coventry. The men were weary, hungry and lacking in powder and shot.

Howe's troops were well-fed, rested and reinforced. They moved forward to their huzzas. They were sure that this battle would bring an end to the nonsense that the ragged Rebels spoke of as their War for Independence.

Washington's positions were on the slopes of steep ridges that mounted sharply above valleys the attacking British had to cross. It was a poor battlefield for Howe's men. But "Old Corncob," as the British Commander-in-Chief's top aide, Major General Charles Cornwallis, was known to the Americans, was sure that the ground made no difference. His troops, he said, could carry any field against the rabble.

His left eye blinking like mad as it always did when he was excited, Cornwallis gave the order to advance. The skirmish lines of each army had just exchanged their first shots when the skies opened and the rain came down.

It was a cloudburst the like of which that part of Pennsylvania had seldom seen. The battlefield was blotted out by the downpour. Shadowy

24

figures showed dimly through the rain curtain for a second and then disappeared. Field commanders desperately tried to keep their companies and regiments in sight and failed. Some troops fired on their comrades. Others let the enemy move past unchallenged.

Washington and his aides were stationed at an observation post high on the mountain. They might as well have been a hundred miles away for all they could see. The clouds that swept in were low-hanging and hovered between the field where the action was taking place and the Command Post. It was an impossible situation for both sides. Then both Washington and Cornwallis got reports that their soldiers were unable to fire a shot because of soaked cartridges and drowned powder horns. Each general ordered a withdrawal.

Some military historians say that if the Americans had taken advantage of the situation right then and there, they might have won their War for Independence at Valley Hill. They point out that many of the American forces occupied lines *above* the rain clouds. These men had dry powder while not one of the attacking British could fire a single bullet.

But other historians point out that the British were experienced with the bayonet while the Americans were not. These experts remind us that the British were stronger than the Americans, numerically and physically. So it is possible that the Redcoats could have carried the field anyway, with cold steel if not with hot shot.

General Wayne wanted to counterattack. He pleaded with Washington to be allowed to loose his Pennsylvanians on the British. But here again confused reports from American scouts made Washington shake his head to Wayne's pleas.

It must be understood that Washington's position was close to desperate. He could not afford to take any chances. Howe and Cornwallis could gamble. If they guessed wrong and lost, there were plenty of reinforcements to fill their ranks. They also had an unlimited flow of supplies coming from Wilmington and landing points on the upper Chesapeake Bay. If Washington took chances and lost, the War for Independence would be over.

By now Washington had no idea of the British strength or of where Howe's units were. He had assigned General William Smallwood of Maryland to watch Howe's movements, but Smallwood's reports were so few and so uncertain that they were almost worse than useless. Why had Smallwood failed in his task? It was because the Americans, outside of Washington and a few others, had no idea of the importance of military intelligence. They sniffed at scouting reports as "fancy fighting" and paid no attention to them.

After the British dragoons had staged a raid to burn precious supplies, a man from Connecticut or North Carolina or Virginia might say, "Uh-huh, I knowed they was goin' to do it. I seed 'em headin' fer there."

"Why didn't you report it, then?"

"Nobody told me to report nothin'. They told me to stand guard at this here post and here I stand."

Washington was bothered by incompetence in many places, ignorance in others and downright double-dealing in still others. Still, he fought to keep his army intact and out of traps set by the British. He also tried to jab a slow-moving and usually indifferent Continental Congress into realizing how his men desperately needed arms and food. Besides this, he had to settle squabbles among members of his own staff and attend to the million and one petty things that should have been cared for by others. That he did not break under the terrible strain seems proof enough that he was sent by Providence to lead America to freedom.

There was no good news, only bad. The British were roving up and down the Schuylkill, stripping the country of hogs and cattle, produce and flour. Sometimes the Redcoats paid for these things with hard gold, and sometimes they took them without paying anything.

If Washington's agents found food, they could offer only poor paper money or receipts to pay for it. Seizing food was forbidden under penalty of the lash. And there were too few farmers in this rich farm area patriotic enough to give their cattle and pigs, their flour and produce, in exchange for a scrawled promise to pay. Even if the farmer was lucky enough to locate the hard-to-find paymaster, his note could be exchanged only for Continental dollars, and they were worth practically nothing.

Such gloomy reports kept coming in. Unlike battle reports these bulletins were correct. Howe's troops destroyed Colonel William Dewees' establishment at Valley Forge on September 18, 1777. French General du Coudray, attached to Washington's staff, drowned because he refused to dismount from his stallion when boarding a flatboat to cross a river. The British were feinting toward

Lancaster and then back at Philadelphia, keeping the Americans off balance. An attack on an important British outpost was never launched because the men sent to make the attack came across a small herd of cattle and broke off the whole campaign to butcher the animals, cook and eat them on the spot.

Even "Mad Anthony" Wayne failed his Commander-in-Chief. Wayne and his forces were camped in the hills near Swedenford when a detachment of British surprised them. The Redcoats used bayonets and sabers to hack surrendered Americans to pieces. So this brief and bloody fight became known as "The Paoli Massacre"; it happened close to the old General Paoli Inn. After that grim incident Wayne was a long time recovering all his high-hearted flair, his reckless charm. He became moody, out-of-sorts, short-tempered, where he had been gay and self-confident before "The Paoli Massacre."

Only one thing more was needed to complete the bleak picture, and on September 27, 1777, it happened. General Howe had practically gutted the Schuylkill Valley of what the Americans needed. The raid on Colonel Dewees' place alone had netted him 4,000 barrels of flour, enough to keep Washington's Army in bread for months. With his foraging completed, Howe entered Philadelphia.

The capital had fallen into British hands.

4

Germantown

THERE REMAINED ONE MORE MAJOR BATTLE TO be fought before the encampment at Valley Forge.

After taking Philadelphia, Howe went into camp at nearby Germantown. Meanwhile Washington rested his troops at Camp Pottsgrove in the Crooked Hills. While there he strengthened his forces with new units. These included a regiment of 400 cavalrymen led by the colorful Polish Count Casimir Pulaski.

The morale of the army rose considerably. Not a little of this rise in spirits was due to the sight of that cavalry regiment. The men wore claret red coats and white buckskin breeches while Pulaski affected a tremendous leathern shako. It was a brave sight to see his horsemen galloping along under a crimson pennant which was marked with a golden eye encircled by thirteen golden stars.

When the Americans moved out of Camp Pottsgrove they headed for Pennypacker Mills. Here supplies were to have been sent from American depots further west. On that march, each man dreamed of a square meal, new boots, a full powder horn, an end to the everlasting shortages. But on reaching their destination, they found nothing. Somebody in the army's wretched supply system had blundered again. And again the growls began in the ranks.

There was plenty to be had in Germantown. Howe's base offered an attractive lure. In Germantown there was food. In Germantown there were cannon and muskets, great stores of supplies and munitions. In Germantown rested a British army that would never believe that the hungry, beaten Patriots would dare attack.

Washington decided to throw a surprise blow at Howe. He had about eleven thousand men, plus two thousand unequipped Virginians who had lately joined his forces. His men were rested, though poorly outfitted. They were anxious to fight, and the Commander-in-Chief thought that the promise of all those supplies that lay within reach would help them fight their best.

"Everything depends on surprise," Washington told his staff. "The enemy expects us to retire to our den and lick our wounds. Let us inflict some wounds on him instead."

The Americans advanced on Germantown on October 4, 1777, by two roads. General Sullivan's New Hampshiremen led the column on the right. The Commander-in-Chief and General Wayne accompanied Sullivan. General Nathaniel

Greene was in command of the column on the left. The two forces struck at the same time.

But the British were not caught napping, as the Americans had hoped. Lack of discipline in the ranks cost Washington his most valuable weapon, the element of surprise. The Americans went down both roads, singing and whooping, firing their muskets into the air, bragging about what they would do to the "bloody Lobsterbacks" when they met up with the enemy.

"Remember Paoli!" they screeched, although their officers ordered them to keep quiet.

Howe's army was ready and waiting. On the right, Sullivan's troops rolled over the British advance guard at the start but stalled. This happened when the British 40th Foot Regiment fortified the Chew House, home of Pennsylvania's Chief Justice Benjamin Chew, a Tory. Instead of passing around the place, the Americans tried to root out the Redcoats there and lost valuable time.

On the left, Greene's troops were in trouble from the start. Howe flung the brunt of his counterattack along this road and smashed the American spearhead in savage fighting.

The weather took a hand here, too. Fog rolled in on Germantown, and the undrilled Americans proved no match for the stolid Germans and the polished English soldiers. The Americans ran helter-skelter, getting in each other's way. The British troops went where they were told, stood when they were told to stand, and fired when they got the order to fire.

Among the Continentals everything was confusion. One general in command of Virginia troops was so drunk he could not tell friend from foe. He had his men fire into the ranks of friendly troops on his left. "Mad Anthony" Wayne was struck in the chest and stunned by a spent bullet. His next-in-command ordered a retreat which exposed Sullivan's flank and threatened General Washington himself with capture.

Drums beat the "retreat." The "surprise" attack had failed. Slowly and with all the high spirits of the day before drooping, the Americans retired, retreating to a camp at Whitemarsh.

The torch of American liberty guttered low. Could it grow any dimmer without flickering out altogether?

George Washington faced his generals over a conference table in his tent at Whitemarsh. Out-

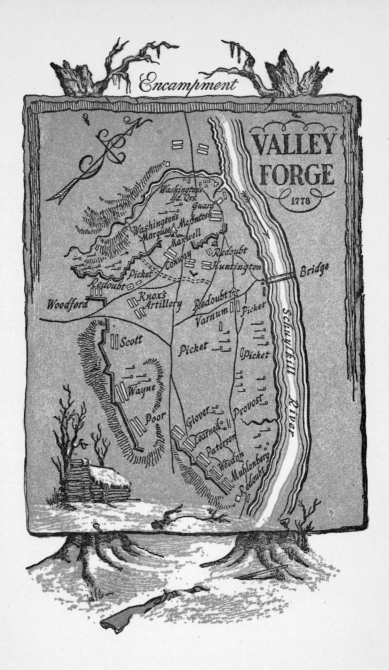

Encampment

VALLEY FORGE

1778

side whistled a chill wind that bore the threat of approaching winter.

"Gentlemen," said the Commander-in-Chief, "we must go into winter quarters at Valley Forge."

5

Into the Valley

GEORGE WASHINGTON HIMSELF WAS NOT ENTHU-
siastic over the choice of Valley Forge as a winter encampment. The Commander-in-Chief would
have preferred to retreat into Maryland or go
further west in Pennsylvania. But as a democratic
leader he put the question to a vote among his
generals. His staff voted to winter at Valley Forge,
ten to five.

There were good arguments in favor of Valley Forge. One of the strongest was the threat by the Pennsylvania Supreme Executive Council to withdraw all support from the army unless it stayed close to Philadelphia that winter.

Others who favored Valley Forge pointed out that it was close to the depots at Warwick and Coventry as well as the arsenals in the Chadd's Ford district. "Lord Stirling" argued that although Colonel Dewees' forge had been wrecked by the British it could be put back in shape for repairing muskets and field pieces. "Lord Stirling" was really an American named William Alexander. He called himself "Lord Stirling" on the grounds that he had been cheated out of a British title.

Still others who were in favor of Valley Forge confidently said that by staying close to Howe, the Americans could raid the British outposts and seize supplies. Then, too, Valley Forge did lie in a good place to draw supplies from Pennsylvania's "bread basket" to the west. If, of course, the farmers who tended the "bread basket" would sell their stock and produce for Continental money.

George Washington must have had many doubts when he approved the majority vote and made plans to move his army to Valley Forge. He knew that being within reaching distance of Coventry and Warwick did not mean much.

By then, the army's supply system had broken down almost completely. For example, while Washington was at Whitemarsh, he asked his supply bases for all the blankets that could be sent him. A wagon train carrying 6,000 blankets was sent, but it went *west* to Lancaster, *away* from Washington's shivering troops. The Commander-in-Chief finally managed to get 200 blankets sent back, but since there was scarcely a whole pair of boots in camp the blankets were mostly cut up and used as foot-wrappings.

Yes, there was food and clothing at Warwick and Coventry and at other depots within reach, but there was nothing in which to move these goods.

Howe's men had drained the area of oxen and draught horses and the few the Americans had were starving for lack of fodder. If an army marches on its stomach, as Napoleon was later to say, that stomach depends on transport. Washington's army had practically no transport at all.

Another man who did not like Valley Forge as a wintering place was "Baron" de Kalb. This man had been born plain Johann Kalb. He had worked as a waiter in Germany before he made himself a

"Baron" while serving with the French as a soldier of fortune and secret agent. De Kalb was a smart officer, but his own choice of winter quarters did not make him seem so. For of all places, de Kalb argued in favor of Wilmington as a winter camp site. He argued strongly. Yet if Washington had put his troops there the army would have been trapped between Howe's forces and the Delaware River.

The winds sharpened, and snow began to fall. Washington's army found itself forced to move into winter quarters with practically none of the stores it required. But move it must, for at least the Valley Forge encampment was better than the Whitemarsh camp to which the Americans had retired after the Battle of Germantown. One by one, the regiments of gaunt, lean men were made ready for the march to Valley Forge, just thirteen miles east of Whitemarsh.

Then, on December 2, 1777, a little old Quaker lady, Lydia Darragh, set out to walk to Philadel-

phia from her farm near Whitemarsh. She bore a
sack of corn meal over her thin shoulders. Lydia
Darragh was a good Quaker. She hated war, but
she also had a nephew who was serving with
Washington. What she knew might save her
nephew from death on the battlefield or imprison-
ment in one of the fever-ridden British jails.

She trudged along the road until she came to an
American outpost. Then she whispered her message to the officer in charge. Somehow she had
learned that Howe, with 5,000 men and thirteen
cannon, was marching to strike the American army
in a surprise attack. After she had delivered her
message Lydia Darragh kept on over the long
miles to Philadelphia. She had told her neighbors
that she was going to Philadelphia, and Lydia Darragh did not believe in telling lies even for a
cause.

This time it was the Americans who were ready,
as the British had been at Germantown. Howe's
forces ran into withering fire at Chestnut Hill. For

one of the few times in this war the "Lobsterbacks" broke and ran. Howe called off the attack and went marching back to Philadelphia.

Washington's losses in that fight were light, but the Americans lost a capable general when Brigadier William Irvine of Pennsylvania was taken prisoner.

Then, too, Howe's foray into the Chestnut Hill region had struck a worse blow at Washington than the damage done by bullet or cannon ball. Before meeting the American forces and turning back, the British rounded up 700 head of cattle in the farming district and herded the precious beef back to Philadelphia for their butchers to deal with.

Now the snow came down in earnest. Ice coated the streams and roads. Washington's army began to move to Valley Forge. The long, wavering column trudged out of Whitemarsh. The Colonials were leaving a camp which held not a single happy memory but they were heading for a place

The numbed marchers staggered slowly on.

that was to provide more misery than men dreamed could be endured.

It was a terrible journey. Only thirteen miles separate Whitemarsh from Valley Forge but it took a full week to move the army from place to place. Every inch of the way was bloodstained by the ice-torn, rag-wrapped feet of the numbed marchers. Men staggered on, fell by the roadside, picked themselves up and staggered on a few more paces. The march resembled a desperate retreat. The question must have been in many minds: if the army is in this condition at the *start* of a winter campaign, what will it be like at the end?

There was no rest for the men when they reached Valley Forge. Huts had to be built. Entrenchments had to be dug. Outposts had to be set up. Guard rosters had to be posted. The meager supplies had to be stored. The various units had to be reorganized and assigned duties.

George Washington was offered comfortable quarters in the old mansion of John Potts, who

had established Mount Joy Forge. This later came
to be known as Valley Forge. Dame Deborah
Hewes, Potts's daughter-in-law, curtsied in the
doorway of her home as the Commander-in-Chief
rode up. She bade him enter and rest, but Washington shook his head.

"A thousand thanks, Madam," the General said,
smiling wearily, "but until my men have their
shelters built, I'll live in my tent. I should be no
warmer than they."

The shelters went up fast. Axmen cut the trees
into sixteen-foot lengths, and the farmer-soldiers
threw up square huts with steeply pitched roofs
in record-breaking time. There was no time for
comforts. The huts had no floors, no windows.
There was a crude fireplace and perhaps a rude
bunk for an officer but none for the men at first.
There was not even time to raise the chimneys to
their proper height. Most chimneys were built too
short to draw properly. All winter men who were
too worn out, too lazy or too ignorant to add to

their chimneys' length coughed and sneezed amid the choking cloud of smoke that filled their cabins.

Slowly Valley Forge assumed the look of a planned position. Along the Schuylkill River to the north, Connecticut and Rhode Island infantry manned the Star Redoubt under the command of Brigadier Generals Jedidah Huntington and Ebenezer Poor. General Sullivan's New Hampshiremen guarded the Flatland Ford, and between the Star Redoubt and Flatland Ford lodged the Pennsylvanians and Delaware's "Blue Hen's Chickens."

On the Outer Line Heights, Pennsylvanians under Wayne and General Thomas Conway joined their units with men from New Hampshire and New Jersey. Other brigades were stationed in likely spots, ready to move to the support of the line units in case of attack. General Henry Knox set up his artillery park in the center of the inner defenses. A commissary which was doomed to be empty most of that winter was established on the King of Prussia Road that led to Pennypacker

Mills. A barn was transformed into the Flying Hospital—a hospital destined to witness scenes of indescribable horror as the winter wore on.

General Washington finally was satisfied that his men were at least under roofs, so he took up his headquarters in the Potts mansion at the northwest corner of the camp. The Commander-in-Chief was surrounded by his Bodyguards. This was the only unit in the whole army that was well trained and well disciplined. It was a high honor to be assigned to the Bodyguards, but some of the 120 men in the company grumbled at that honor when they were routed from their pallets at three o'clock in the morning. That was first time drill for the Bodyguards under the lashing tongue of a crusty disciplinarian named Baron Frederick Augustus Henry Ferdinand von Steuben.

"This," von Steuben used to say as he pointed at the Bodyguards with the walking stick he always carried, "is my military academy. They come to me knowing not their right foot from their left, or their heads from their hands. When I send them back to their brigades they can drill troops better than their generals."

This was true. Von Steuben was a harsh taskmaster, but he made soldiers. His "military academy" graduates returned to their units well prepared to train their comrades. The Bodyguards gave Washington's army a rigid backbone it had needed for a long time.

The winter closed down. The temperatures sank. The snow piled high, choking the roads. Hunger moved in. While Washington's men starved at Valley Forge, huge supplies of beef and pork rotted in New Jersey. This meat was kept from the famished soldiers because there were no animals to haul it and no open roads to haul it on. Thousands of barrels of flour spoiled on the banks of the Susquehanna River, not far from Valley Forge, because there was no transport to move them a few miles to the hungry troops.

Orders from Headquarters still said: No foraging. Anyone caught stealing from the farmers was given a hundred lashes. Yet the risk of having one's back laid open by a cruel whip did not stop many a famished Continental from "requisitioning" a plump goose, a tasty hen, a "stray" pig or even a "wandering" cow.

And who could blame these men? Their rations had been cut and cut until now they were practically nothing. The troops lived off the tough and tasteless "firecakes" and drank melted snow water. And at Reading, the man in charge of supplying Washington's army sulked and plotted. This was Major General Thomas Mifflin who wanted General Horatio Gates to be Commander-in-Chief instead of Washington. He was too busy plotting against Washington to be bothered with the work of supplying the men at Valley Forge. It became a case of "root hog, or die" for the Americans.

Then Hunger's dread companion, Disease, swept Valley Forge. The American forces were struck by smallpox and "camp fever" which we call typhus today. Gangrene that made rotting stumps of frozen hands and feet took a dreadful toll. There was no medicine. There were only a few surgeons. Even such a simple thing as a clean bandage was at a premium.

The camp became a charnel house as saddle horses starved, died and lay where they fell. There had always been too many officers' mounts and not enough draught animals. Now the pet mares and stallions of the gentlemen from Virginia and Maryland, York State and Pennsylvania, died by the dozens. Human bodies and amputated parts of bodies lay in shallow trenches.

These were the days before men knew about germs. Epidemics were blamed on "vapours." A wound was left to fester because pus was believed to be a healing agent. Blood transfusions were unheard of. Instead, the doctors would drain blood from men already weak from hunger and disease.

Three thousand men answered the first Sick Call at Valley Forge. That was more than a quarter of

Washington's whole force. In January, 1778, more than a third of Washington's officers and men were unable to get to their feet to answer roll call. More than half of those present for duty were in ranks only because their courage was stronger than the fevers that wracked them.

What kept them from deserting in droves? What forced them from their sickbeds to stand swaying in ranks? Whence came the spirit that helped these men bite back their complaints? What strength of faith must have guided men like Richard Wheeler of New York State? He wrote home to his folks that January to say that he was "very Comfittable & Liveing off the Fatt of the Land." Such letters gave the lie to the British and the Tories' true reports of starvation and sickness in Washington's camp.

Not everybody was a hero. Many officers resigned their commissions and went home. Even "Mad Anthony" Wayne threatened to desert unless he was given leave. His leave was not given, but

Wayne stayed on, of course. Chaplains returned to their home pulpits because the men were too weak, too frozen, too hungry, to listen to their long sermons. Soldiers caught trying to desert were lashed or shot. But for every man who quit or tried to quit, there were a dozen others who had no thought of quitting. These men had little but defeat to look back upon. They had nothing, not even food or boots at hand. They had no visible hopes for the future, but they stayed loyal to their cause of Freedom.

"These are the times that try men's souls," wrote Thomas Paine. And the most savage winter in the memory of the Colonies hurled its icy might against the Americans at Valley Forge to add to the miserable fortunes of war. Washington's men bent beneath the test, but they did not break.

And all the world watched and wondered.

Even in the darkest days of Valley Forge there were new men coming into camp, volunteering for what they could plainly see would be a life of misery.

Two of these new recruits, two typical soldiers of Washington's Army, were Gilbert Weston of Massachusetts and his friend, a Micmac Indian. Uksene-ak, also called Silver Hawk, came from the northern tip of Massachusetts, now known as Maine.

6

Supply Train

THE TWO VOLUNTEERS WERE ON THEIR WAY TO offer their services with General John Glover's Massachusetts Brigade. They headed for Valley Forge with a four-wagon supply train trying to struggle through to the winter encampment.

A cold and rising wind out of the northwest stirred snow that already was lying deep on the road. The tiny, stinging particles warned of another blizzard on the way. Wearily, the brown and white ox teams leaned into their yokes and closed their frost-rimmed eyes against the mounting gale.

At the top of a long, sloping incline a copse of dark firs swayed uneasily under the heavy blasts

of the gathering storm. The wagon train's commander, Lieutenant Freeman of Conway's Pennsylvania Brigade, knew that beyond those woods he would sight a wide area of farm land sloping gently toward the hard-frozen Schuylkill River and Valley Forge.

On either side of the leading cart marched a

pair of guards, Gil Weston and Silver Hawk. Weston, the larger of the two, might have been seventeen. He was tall and gangling but strongly built none the less. Both he and the Micmac, his companion, wore Indian-made buckskin moccasins and leggings over coarse trousers. Heavy gray flannel shirts and thick, badly worn, gray serge jackets completed their unmilitary garb.

Gil lugged a powder horn and a huge Tower musket. Uksene-ak, light complexioned as were most Micmacs, was armed with a short war bow. This he carried in a buckskin case decorated with porcupine quills. He also carried a knife and one of those light war hatchets that the Mohawks could throw with such deadly precision.

"*Nesako Muen*—Tall Bear, my brother," the young Indian called over the snowy backs of the oxen, "this weather will soon become bad, very bad. Let us hope our officer will make camp in that grove."

Gil Weston nodded his moth-eaten fox fur cap.

"Yep. If I know anything about it these here critters are just about played out."

Behind them, Sergeant Larkin pricked the broad rumps of the lead span of oxen with his goad. Then he bellowed back over his shoulder: "Hi, Lieutenant! Hadn't we best halt and let the rest ketch up? Might be some o' Simcoe's murderin' Green Jackets loose and we've got ourselves strung out over nigh half a mile."

The Lieutenant's voice came back thinly, whipped by the driving snow. "We'll close up in the lee of those woods ahead when we get to the top of the hill. Don't worry—even Britishers and Tories have got more sense than to go gallivanting around in this kind of weather."

Uksene-ak eyed the crest of the ridge ahead uneasily. There the firs marched down to the very edge of the road and in these woods. . . . Seized by a sudden fear, the young Indian started to trot out ahead of the blowing oxen. Immediately Sergeant Larkin set up a bellow.

"Come back here, you heathen savage!" he bawled. "Who in tunket told you to go strayin' off?"

Gil Weston's broad, wind-reddened face tightened. Until a short time before he had not realized how completely mistrusted and feared were any and all Indians here in Eastern Pennsylvania. This, in spite of the fact that a hostile savage had not raided in these parts in nearly a hundred years. He waded through a snowdrift toward the ponderous, high-wheeled cart.

"Say, Sergeant," he explained. "Hawk don't mean no harm, but like me he figgers they just might be somebody layin' fer us beyond that rise."

"Don't recall askin' your opinion, Bub," spat the Sergeant. "Hold your tongue and git back in line."

Larkin hunched over on the seat and blew a bulbous red nose with his fingers. Gil started to speak. Then he remembered his father's parting advice: "Ye'll git ahead in the Army if you salute plenty and don't argue with your superiors."

Pa ought to know. As a militiaman he had marched against the French and the Indians and had won himself a battlefield commission at Louisburg in 1745. Gil left his answer to Sergeant Larkin unsaid. He shifted the six-foot-long musket Pa had carried in the wars and went back to his position beside the off ox.

He looked back to see the men from Conway's Brigade stumbling along in knee-deep snow. Their heads were bent against the wind. They were carrying an amazing assortment of weapons and no two of the ragged, scarecrow figures were dressed alike. Some wore the faded remnants of summer uniforms. Others risked the warmth of scarlet jackets captured from the enemy even though their friends might use them for targets. Most of them struggled along in the gray, brown and black civilian coats scavenged from Heaven alone knew where.

The sky darkened steadily, taking on a threatening leaden-white color. Silver Hawk had been all too good a weather prophet. That morning he had warned of a blizzard on its way, another of the long series that had plagued Pennsylvania that winter.

Suddenly Gil's head swung sharply to the right. Something had flickered in the depths of the evergreen woods—something red! Of course, it might have been a cardinal bird, but . . .

Then came a whoop from Silver Hawk. It was the shrill, ear-piercing howl of a Micmac war cry! In the next second a swarm of mounted men charged out of the evergreens. They wore brass helmets, green tunics with white cross-belts, and flapping gray cloaks. In their van was a British dragoon officer in the scarlet uniform Gil had glimpsed.

"Simcoe's Green Jackets!" Sergeant Larkin roared. "Tories!"

His cry was drowned out by the boom of carbines and the crack of pistols as the raiders swooped down on the wagon train. The guards among the strung-out carts yelled in terror. They tried to fire the weapons they had wrapped in rags against the powdery snow. But too many of the flintlocks' pans and priming had been wet. There were only a few answering shots to the Tory fusillade.

Gil raised Pa's heavy old Brown Bess musket and let fly point-blank at a big raider who came spurring at him with saber leveled at Gil's chest.

Boo-o-oom!

Gil's vision was obscured by the gagging smoke that blossomed out. It cleared enough to let him see the trooper's horse rear up, up, up, until its rider tumbled onto the snow. The scarlet lining of his gray cape showed as raw as a vast wound.

Lieutenant Freeman shrilled orders and then fell with a scream of mortal agony. Gil crouched to reload his musket. He knew that only three or four of the train guard had been able to fire a reply to the Tories. There could be little hope for him and the others of the ambushed supply column.

"Quarter! Quarter! For God's sake spare us!"

65

Shrill yelps of terror sounded down the length of the wagon train.

Sergeant Larkin was not one of those who yelled. Just as a snarling Queen's Ranger drove at him the thick-bodied Pennsylvanian reached beneath his wagon's seat and pulled out a saber and pistol. The oxen lurched, panic-stricken, and Silver Hawk saw Larkin's pistol shot go wild. The Micmac nocked an arrow to his war bow.

The gray-cloaked Tory pulled back his saber for a certain death stroke at Larkin. Then he flinched and twisted in his saddle, cursing. The bloody head of an arrow poked out of his right shoulder. Under the wrenching of its rider's reins the Tory's horse circled crazily, reared and threw the Queen's Ranger.

"Get down, Sergeant!" yelled the young Indian. "Get into woods!"

Larkin flung himself off the cart as a pair of Rangers came plowing through the drifted snow toward the stalled lead wagon. Gil cast a fleeting glance down the road. Drivers and guards of the other carts were kneeling, defenseless. They raised empty hands in the biting, snow-filled air.

As Gil scurried to take cover among the firs and spruces he spied the trim, brass-mounted carbine of the Ranger he had killed. He plunged over to retrieve it, feeling sick. For all the many deer and moose he had killed in his day he never before had hurt, let alone slain, a human.

The cavalry carbine was a far handier weapon for a boy of Gil's size than Pa's clumsy old Tower musket. Gil slid behind the bole of a fir tree and fired the stubby piece at one of the plunging horsemen before fading farther back into the grove.

Panting, he reloaded. Silver Hawk and the Sergeant, he reckoned, must be on the far side of the road. The Tories, enraged over this unexpected opposition, were out for revenge. He dropped back farther to find shelter under the snow-covered branches of a giant spruce. His tracks were covered by the trampling of the Tory horses. There he crouched, as motionless as a snowshoe rabbit, his homespun coat warm about him.

Faintly, through the whine of the wind and the hiss of the sleety snow, he heard the harsh British voice of Major John Simcoe. The red-uniformed dragoon who led the Queen's Rangers ordered his prisoners to start their carts back along the road toward Pennypacker Mills.

"Hah!" Gil heard a Tory shout. "The Rebels will have to eat snow now! This makes the third food convoy cut off this week! They deserve to starve!"

He stayed where he was, scarcely breathing, as the Green Jackets made off with the captured train and their dead and wounded. He waited a good half hour after the last sounds of the departing enemy came down the wind. Then he sent up the call of the great horned owl. Twice, then three times, he sent the feathered night killer's cry quavering through the forest. Then he relaxed in relief as a fox yapped from behind a rocky knoll across the way.

Gil wormed through the snow and peered over a snow-covered rock beside the roadway. Across from him Silver Hawk's impassive face peered around a holly clump.

"Silver Hawk," Gil called, "are you hurt, my brother?"

"No, *Muen*." The Micmac cautiously slipped out of the holly clump and edged toward the road.

"Is the Sergeant with you?" Gil queried.

"Yes, but I left him behind. He makes too much noise."

They came upon Sergeant Larkin crouching miserably under an overhanging ledge. He had lost his hat in the scramble of the attack and his dull red hair was snow-powdered nearly as white as that of a British grenadier on parade.

"Well," the Pennsylvanian grunted, " 'pears like we're luckier than them that got took—but not

69

much. It's comin' on dark, and it's gettin' fit to freeze a man solid. Dunno what we can do."

"Could we get to Valley Forge?" Gil asked.

"Unh-unh. 'Tis near eight miles to the outposts, even if we could find 'em in this blasted storm. We'd likely fall into a ravine and freeze." Larkin swung his arms heavily to restore circulation. "Bein' as how we ain't got no blankets, wish we could build us a fire. But 'tain't no use to even try in this wind, I s'pose."

Silver Hawk looked about him and grunted. He pointed to a chestnut tree with a forked trunk in the ravine below the ledge.

"*Wagh*," the Micmac murmured. "*Weelolin*. We camp there."

The Indian's hatchet and Gil's knife quickly shaped a lean-to. Sergeant Larkin, meanwhile, busied himself at building a fireplace of loose rocks. In spite of the whirling, snow-clouded wind, Gil managed to scrape steel against flint and set fire to a soft nest of bark shredded from a dead cedar. Soon the three men had heat and shelter.

"You fellers got a mite to eat, mebbe?" the Sergeant asked.

"Only a hunk of Army bread," Gil confessed. "They gave us a little at Norristown."

Silver Hawk silently offered a small greasy leather pouch.

"Pemmican," he explained, briefly.

"What in tarnation's pemmican?" asked the burly Pennsylvanian.

"Dried venison," Gil said. "It tastes terrible, and it smells worse but it's plenty nourishin', Sergeant."

The three survivors of the wagon train raid lay close together in the lean-to, chewing pemmican and swallowing army bread that was so hard that Silver Hawk had to use his war hatchet to split it. In spite of the fire it was miserably cold. Outside the reach of the campfire's heat a man surely would freeze to death in a matter of minutes.

"Reckon we'd better take turns feedin' the fire," Larkin said, yawning. "I'm plumb fagged out. Injun, you stand first watch."

"I'll take second watch," Gil nodded. "We'll make out till dawn unless somebody spies our fire that hadn't ought to."

7

Hungry Encampment

"WE'LL SIGHT THE ENCAMPMENT FROM THE summit of yonder rise." Sergeant Larkin coughed. "Then you'll see more human misery than you'll ever find this side of eternal punishment."

"As bad as that?" Gil asked. He blew hard on hands half protected by shabby woolen mittens.

"Aye. Yonder's the reason." Larkin jerked his muffler-shrouded head to the left. There stood the charred remnants of a little farmhouse. Its black-

73

ened stone walls rose starkly from the snow. "You'll see many a place like that. All of 'em, pretty near, were wiped out by the Lobsterbacks."

Presently the three half-frozen travelers reached a crossroads marked by a signpost. One of the weatherbeaten finger boards showed that Perkiomen lay to the north. Another pointed to the east where it said the King of Prussia Tavern was situated. A third indicated that the road ahead led to Mount Joy Forge.

"That's Valley Forge," Sergeant Larkin explained. " 'Twas a useful foundry to us Patriots, too, till the Redcoats burned Colonel Dewees out last fall."

Gil trudged along with the captured carbine on his shoulder. He laughed silently at the sight of the Sergeant lugging Pa's musket. Larkin complained continually about the eleven-pound weight of the Tower. But since he had lost his own pistol and saber, he knew he had better have something

74

to show by way of replacement when he returned to his company.

Silver Hawk uttered a grunt and pointed to a snow-swept corn field on their left. Through the scurrying snow whirls Gil made out the outline of a horse. It was standing with its head held low and its skinny rump turned into the wind. The poor beast's ribs stood out under a coating of snow as it stood there, awaiting its doom.

"Ye'll see plenty of them poor critters around," Larkin said. "Our artillery nags and officers' mounts is perishin' fer want of fodder." The Sergeant shook his head. "Say, boys," he added, "let's put him out of his misery. Ain't no meat on that carcass, but the liver and lights might be good."

A half hour later they were on their way again, having finished the wretched but still humane business of dispatching the horse. Their progress was slow as they struggled through snow that often came up to their waists. Sergeant Larkin swore lustily whenever a hard crust hidden by the new snowfall further ripped his coarse woolen socks. Gil noticed that the Pennsylvanian's boots gaped like the jaws of a hungry pike. The twine used to lash the soles to their uppers had worn through.

"Whereat is your outfit, Sergeant?" Gil asked as the three started down a slope toward the Schuylkill River.

"I'm with Wayne and he's 'way off to the southwest, below the artillery park. Ye kin see if you look sharp."

Silver Hawk's keen gaze detected a cluster of huts lying across a wide plain in the distance. Nearer at hand thin wisps of smoke rose from the rude wood and clay chimneys of a row of cabins by the river's edge. Few of the eleven thousand troops encamped at Valley Forge were in sight. Only the tiny figures of wood-cutting parties and building crews could be seen here and there, working at felling trees and putting up new huts.

"What regiment you fixin' to join?" Larkin

asked while he and his young companions half-slipped, half-slid down toward the wide level ribbon that marked the frozen Schuylkill.

"Glover's," Gil said. He eased the weight of the haversack he carried. The canvas bag bulged with the remains of the horse meat.

"Why jine up with them durned Yankees?" the Sergeant asked.

"I had an uncle with Glover's Brigade till he died of camp fever at a place called White-marsh," Gil explained.

"Late last fall?" Larkin queried.

"Yep. He was wounded afore that in a big battle. I disremember the name of it."

"Must've been Germantown," grunted the Pennsylvanian. "Last October. I was there." He turned a chapped and swollen red face toward the boy from Massachusetts. "If ye're smart, ye'll join Wayne's."

"Why?" came Silver Hawk's unexpected query.

" 'Cause they're so desprit fer scouts and

77

woodsmen the Gen'ral will enlist anybody—even a heathen savage. Besides, they're so bad off with fever they're 'way below strength." He shifted the big musket to his other shoulder with a groan. "Still, y'might do better with Glover's at that. Gen'ral ain't here hisself right now, but his son John commands their First Company. Mebbe he'll favor you, on account of your uncle served there. Mebbe he won't. Hard people, them Yankees—meaner than a she-wolf with pups, most times."

As the three soldiers crossed the river, some sentries clad in ragged dark blue cloaks and wearing sacks stuffed with straw in place of boots challenged listlessly. A blue-lipped lieutenant shuffled forward.

"That you, Larkin?" he asked. "Where's the rest of your detail? *Where are the supply wagons?*"

"On their way to Philadelphy, I reckon, sir," was Larkin's dismal reply.

"Don't tell me that that food was lost!" In the officer's hollow eyes shone stark despair.

"Aye. A big party of Tories jumped us last evenin' on the Perkiomen Road."

A groan arose from the knot of sniffling, shaggy, red-nosed men who emerged from a rough wigwam fashioned of fir boughs. Silver Hawk had lived through *Segon-goos*, the famine season in Nova Scotia, but he could not remember men who looked hungrier than these poor specimens.

The young Micmac wondered what kept these wretched white men on their feet. When the war-

riors of his tribe realized that stored food had given out and no more was to be had, they retired to a corner of their wigwams, hauled a robe over their heads and patiently awaited death by freezing. Still these frail creatures struggled on. Surely, he thought, these men must have strong medicine!

"Food gone?" one of the sentries groaned. "That means firecake and water again tonight."

"Surely," Silver Hawk told himself, "that man's hand is frozen."

Peering into the guard hut, the Micmac saw the gaunt, yellow-gray outlines of two naked men lying on the bare ground. Obviously they were dead. They had frozen stiff, and their clothes had been stripped from them by their companions.

"A pity," the officer said as he turned away from Sergeant Larkin. "We've been countin' on a little meat tonight."

"Didn't *any* wagons git away?" wistfully asked a gap-toothed Corporal who wore a faded red worsted knot, the emblem of his rank, on his left shoulder. "Not even one?"

"Nary one," Larkin said. "Durned Green Jackets jumped us when we was all strung out. Didn't have a chance."

"Say, what you got in that bag?" The Corporal was pointing at Gil's haversack.

"Nothin'," Sergeant Larkin snapped. "Just his gear and bullet mold."

"Then where'd that fresh blood come from, hey?"

"Here," Silver Hawk said quickly. He bared a lean brown wrist. The Micmac had suffered very recently a shallow thorn gash across his forearm.

Gil wished desperately to share the contents of his haversack with these famished men but a warning of Larkin's rang in his ears: "Ye'll find some pretty hard characters among Glover's. They know how to make life mighty miserable for a recruit. Jest you young fellers hang onto your food

—till it can buy some friendship fer you where it'll count."

Now the two newcomers to Valley Forge and the returned Sergeant moved past the sentries. They trudged over a rutted, snow-packed road to a group of log huts half buried in the drifts.

"I say good-bye to ye here," Larkin snuffled. "Good luck. Wish ye could join up here 'cause ye're a handy pair and no mistake." He jerked his head toward the southwest. "Me, I've got to break the bad news to Cap'n Baldwin. I've got to tell him he's out twenty men, besides some oxen and carts. Not to mention all them vittles."

He hesitated, looking a trifle sheepish.

"Bub," he went on to Gil, "if ye don't mind, I'll hang onto this musket of your Pa's. I won't look quite such a fool if I got a gun when I show up afore Cap'n Baldwin. Ye kin git it back later, after I snitch another somewheres."

"You're welcome to it," Gil said.

"Ye know how t'find Glover's?" Larkin said.

"Ye go that way and to your left. Ask anybody; they'll show ye." He turned to Silver Hawk and spoke hesitantly. "Good luck, Injun," he said. "And—and thanks. 'Twas your arrer that saved my bacon in the ambush, and I won't fergit it."

8

Enlistment

IN A COW SHED THAT SERVED AS HEADQUAR-
ters for Brigadier General John Glover's Massachusetts Brigade the air hung heavy with eye-
stinging smoke and the reek of bodies too long
unwashed. The tiny shed was jam-packed, not only
with staff officers and their clerks but also with
messengers, orderlies and any other soldiers who
could find an excuse for lingering out of the icy
cold.

84

Gil Weston and Silver Hawk stood before a rough wooden table. Behind it sat a stolid individual. He wore a faded blue tunic with once-white lapels and revers which were brown now with spots, smudges and stains. Around his neck Captain Joseph Swazey had fastened a woman's tippet of bedraggled fox fur. He kept using his knuckles to brush away a stream of tears caused by the smoke.

"I'm sorry, Weston," Swazey was saying. "I can't enroll you or your Indian friend in my company, much as I'd like to. Your uncle, Archer Weston, made one of the best and bravest sergeants I ever had."

"But Captain Swazey, sir," Gil protested, "Uksene-ak and me ain't neither of us big, and we don't eat much. Besides, we can make ourselves mighty useful in the woods. Really we can, sir."

The commanding officer of Third Company sighed and shook his head.

"Believe me, Gil," he said, "had I but any free

85

space in our huts and if we weren't already on quarter rations, I'd enlist you straight off. But I can't."

Silver Hawk's olive-hued face remained expressionless as he spoke.

"Uksene-ak has come far, come from Kespoogwit, to serve you, my Father. If you will take us into your band, Gil, my Brother, and I will find our own food and shelter."

Captain Swazey smiled faintly but shook his head again.

"I can't go against Colonel Glover's orders," he explained. "Why don't you join up with Captain Allan McLain's Oneida Scouts? You're both frontier bred."

Emphatically Gil shook his head.

"Impossible, sir!"

"And why?"

"The Oneidas are one of the Six Nations of the Iroquois, and the Micmacs and Iroquois are sworn enemies."

"I see," Swazey nodded. "Well, here's another suggestion. Why don't you enlist in Wayne's Brigade? Mad Anthony's got a lot of city men who don't know 'come here' from 'sic 'em' about caring for themselves in the open. He'd likely welcome two woods-wise foragers like you."

The two youths set out over the trampled fields toward the western edge of the camp. They were nearing a row of half-completed log huts when Silver Hawk grunted and pointed at a row of low, irregular mounds of snow. Gil was sickened when he saw that from one of these piles there thrust a hand and naked arm. Two mounds farther on, the wind had uncovered a pair of human legs. One was marked by a gangrenous wound. Gil swallowed hard and turned away.

Captain Bartow of the Fourth Company of Wayne's Brigade was a long, lean individual with whitish stubble sprouting from his lantern jaw.

"Sure, I'll enlist you," he said, coughing. "Ever since we reached this cursed place my men have been dying like rats in a trap. Sign, or make your mark, right here. You, Weston, I mean—not this savage."

"But sir, I was speakin' for both of us," Gil protested.

"We don't want any treacherous redskins in the Fourth," Bartow snarled.

"I'm sorry, sir," Gil said steadily. "Silver Hawk and I enlist together or I don't join up."

The Captain's long horse face contracted. "You claim this Injun's handy at foraging?" he asked bluntly.

"Yes, sir."

"Very well. Let him make his mark."

After Gil had signed and Uksene-ak had made the sign of the hawk, Captain Bartow offered a large chapped hand to Weston.

"Good luck, son," he said. "I think you're going to need it on account of you being a New Englander. Yankees aren't exactly popular, especially in Corporal Cassidy's squad where you're going. They hate New England for having started this war, most of 'em."

Corporal Cassidy proved to be a loud, hulking fellow with the voice, the strength and the intelligence of a bull. He dominated the starving, spiritless wretches under him with savage enjoyment.

"Lucifer blast me!" he roared when Gil and Silver Hawk appeared at the hut's door. "What do you cubs want here?"

Gil showed his assignment slip written by Captain Bartow's clerk.

"So 'tis recruits ye're supposed to be?" rasped Cassidy. " 'Tis sure now we've reached the bottom of the barrel! What've you whelps got in them knapsacks?"

Gil gulped. "Why, we brought along something for the squad, some horse liver and kidneys and some b-b-brains."

"Food! Food!" From under a scattering of

89

ragged blankets figures roused up from the dirt floor of this smoke-filled hut. "Food! Did somebody say food?"

"Give me that!" Cassidy's hand shot out, snatching away first Silver Hawk's haversack and then Gil's. A pot was produced and snow shoveled into it. A fire in the wood and clay fireplace was prodded so that it smoked worse than ever.

"I'll take that fur jacket," growled a dark-bearded soldier. "It ain't fitten fer a savage to go warm whilst a white man shivers."

"*Ankodum*—look out!" The Micmac's hand flew toward the war hatchet at his belt. But another of the gaunt Pennsylvanians brought a piece of firewood crashing down on the Indian's coonskin cap. Uksene-ak dropped without a sound.

Gil Weston lashed out furiously. He landed a solid punch on the jaw of the man who clubbed Silver Hawk. Then Corporal Cassidy's hamlike hand closed over his shoulder and spun him about. The Irishman dealt him a body blow that

90

drove the breath out of him and filled his eyes
with whirling green and red stars.

"Faith, and you pups will have to learn man-
ners!" the Corporal growled. He kicked the Indian when he sat up, a trickle of blood oozing
down his face from under the blue-black hair.

"Get out, ye heathen, and fetch us some fire-wood!"

The next few days were bad ones for Gil and Silver Hawk. Cassidy bullied the recruits until even the sick and starving members of his squad protested. There was nothing for food except a single panful of coarse-ground corn that was fetched back to the hut from the Quartermaster's store each day. Biting winds kept blowing fine snow through the chinking between the logs. It was too cold to drill. The weather was too bad for anything except to crouch about the fireplace, dozing fitfully. Men died by the dozens in nearby huts. Silver Hawk and Gil were browbeaten into the hardest and most menial tasks. At night they would lie together, wrapped in a single thin blanket, miserably listening to the wind moan through the cracks in the walls.

The artillery horses and officers' mounts now began dying by the hundreds although there was feed for them, and to spare, not thirty miles away.

In Reading lay great supplies of warm uniforms, food and blankets. Reading was only thirty-five miles distant, but it might as well have been in China for all the good those supplies did the men who were freezing in Valley Forge.

"Ever been this hungry?" Gil whispered one night as he and Hawk lay shivering in the icy darkness.

"Aye. The Indians always have a starving season late in the winter. Tonight, *Muen*, my brother, we go hunting. We must eat or we, too, shall fall sick and die. We must find food since the corporal will not give us even our little share."

"*Kway, Wetaak*. Yes, it sounds well," Gil said. He heaved himself up on one elbow. "There's a moon tonight so it should be light enough to see by." He began groping for his carbine, but Silver Hawk shook his head.

"Leave it," the Indian said. "To shoot would rouse the sentries and bring us trouble."

Corporal Cassidy and the rest of the squad lay

huddled together like piles of castoff clothing. Their heads were almost resting in the ashes of the hearth. Their breath showed white against the fire in silvery puffs. Gil and Silver Hawk slipped out of the hut.

It was absurdly easy to sneak out of the encampment. The chilled sentries on duty at that hour were gathered about their little watch fires. They saw nothing of the two slight figures who twisted and turned noiselessly through the ice-coated underbrush.

"There's an old corn field beyond the artillery park," Gil whispered. "But of course there's not a grain of corn left there."

"Let us seek the birch woods two fields beyond," the Indian murmured.

"Good idea. I think there's another corn field somewheres about there, too."

Their feet crunched crisply on a crust which fortunately was thick enough to support their weight. The moon shone with a chill, cold light. It revealed in sharp relief the farmhouses that had been burned by the raiding British the previous fall. The boys traveled a good two miles before they came upon a second corn field.

Foragers had long since gathered such undeveloped ears as the harvesters had overlooked. Most of the corn shocks had been carried off for bedding but fresh rabbit tracks indicated that at least a scattering of kernels had been left behind. When they reached a grove of slender young birches beyond the corn field, Silver Hawk held up his hand. Gil watched the Micmac pull an arrow from his quiver. After signaling Gil to wait, Uksene-ak slipped soundlessly into a thicket.

Once, twice, Gil heard the deep *hum-m-m* of a loosed bowstring. When an owl called softly, he moved silently through the snow until he came upon his Indian friend. Silver Hawk's teeth gleamed in a brief grin. He held up the body of a rabbit speared by an arrow. It took only a few moments to skin the animal. Then both youngsters tore at the warm, tender meat.

Before dawn three more rabbits lay in Silver Hawk's knapsack. Gil had skillfully rigged half a dozen leather thong snares over various rabbit runs. As they traveled back to their hut they crossed a clearing surrounded by the foundations and charred remains of a burned barn. Silver Hawk halted and pointed toward what suggested a row of grotesque fat faces peering over a stone fence. The Micmac strode to the fence and lopped off one of the "heads."

"What in tarnation do you want with them no-good old sunflowers?" Gil asked in an undertone.

"Let *Muen*, my brother, be patient and he will learn."

Corporal Cassidy was astounded when into the squad's common cooking pot Gil slipped three skinned rabbit carcasses.

"Well, Bub, may I be boiled in oil!" he roared. "Now where in the world did you find these lovely little critters?"

"Ask the useless red savage you're so fond of tormenting," Gil replied bitterly. "If you'll let up on Silver Hawk and me I shouldn't wonder but what this squad all might have a bread of a sort before long."

"Ye kin do what ye please," grunted the Corporal, "so long's ye git us the food."

About midday Silver Hawk fashioned thick round cakes of hulled and crushed sunflower seeds. These proved to be surprisingly tasty and nutritious when cooked among the embers. After that there was no more talk about a "sniveling Yankee" and a "worthless young savage" in the hut of Corporal Cassidy's squad.

9
Headquarters

JANUARY, 1778, WAS A MONTH OF UNBELIEVABLY
cold weather. Famine stalked the encampment.
The Fourth Squad of the Fourth Company,
Wayne's Brigade, however, fared better than their
neighbors. Gil cut a window in the hut, used
a partially smoked cow's bladder for a pane, and
thus dispelled the perpetual gloom. Now the soldiers could see to clean their equipment and make
such rude improvements as shelves, stools and pegs

on which to hang their muskets and sodden garments.

The Micmac found a bee tree and taught the shoeless men of the squad how to coat their feet with warm beeswax. This precaution kept out the wet and protected the skin against chilblains. The

two young friends made life more bearable for their squadmates in a dozen ways.

One day Gil was summoned to Captain Bartow's hut. Said that cadaverous officer:

"Weston, here's the Company's strength report and a requisition. Of course, the requisition won't get us anything but I may as well go on record. You're to carry these over to the Commissary Office at General Headquarters." He scowled. "Don't you dare come back, young fellow, without at least the *promise* of ten overcoats and a wagonload of straw—when and if they ever get through to Valley Forge."

General Washington's Headquarters lay diagonally from the encampment of Wayne's Brigade. Gil's route took him past Brigadier General Charles Scott's Virginia troops, the park of Major General Knox's artillery, and so up to the Old Gulph Road.

Today the sun shone, and the cold had moderated enough to permit some units to break out for close order drill. In front of Jedidah Huntington's Connecticut Brigade Headquarters, field punishment was being given some offenders. In slovenly ranks the troops were drawn up in a hollow square about a heavy wooden triangle to which a man had been tied. A big sergeant had rolled up his sleeves and, using a three-foot lash, was laying on the prescribed number of stripes so lustily that the punished man's screams rent the air.

"Wha-what's he done?" Gil asked a passing woodcutter.

"Gittin' two hundred fer stealin' a hat from his mate," the man explained cheerfully. "My, ain't that sergeant makin' his back *smoke* though!"

Washington's Bodyguards were quartered across Valley Creek from the stone mansion which was Washington's Headquarters. At the moment, several units were attempting some squad movements under the eye of a massive, red-faced officer in a huge tricorn hat and ankle-length gray cloak with a fur collar. He carried a long walking stick which he waved as he gave his orders in a deep roaring voice.

Gil lingered to watch. These troops were the best drilled that he had ever seen. They dressed ranks much better than those of Wayne's or Glover's. A dismounted cavalryman came striding along, his curved saber tucked under an arm.

"What's going on over there?" Gil asked the passer-by.

"Oh, that's the old Dutchman, General von Steuben. He's tryin' to knock some notions of European drill into the Commander-in-Chief's Bodyguards." The cavalryman scratched vigorously under his tunic. "They're good soldiers, them Bodyguards. Old von Steuben's got the temper of a fiend dipped in holy water, they say. And he's sure got a voice like the Bull of Bashan, ain't he?"

A semicircle of couriers' and officers' mounts stamped and steamed before a well-gnawed hitching post in front of Headquarters. A bewildering galaxy of uniforms was to be seen. Here were Pulaski's Lancers in gaudy claret and silver. There went the French officers attached to Washington's staff, wearing blue, white or green uniforms, all a-glitter with silver and gold lace.

There were few gold buttons and little gold lace among the Americans. Their units could only be guessed at by the revers, or lapels of their tunics. The Virginians wore buff revers, Maryland and Delaware wore blue, Pennsylvanians wore red, and Massachusetts and New Hampshire wore white.

Gil walked on. He felt very young and very unmilitary in his stained and frayed Indian leggings, the bedraggled fox fur cap, the leather breeches and the civilian homespun coat. As he went his way, he saw several officers whom he recognized. There was the Chief of Artillery, bluff General Knox. There was pompous Brigadier General Weedon of Virginia. There was neat and capable Major General Nathaniel Greene who had just been named to the post of Quartermaster-General of the Army. General Greene, he noticed, walked with a limp that was caused by a malformed foot.

Most of all, Gil wanted to lay eyes on that gay and gallant redhead, the Marquis de Lafayette.

He had heard that the young Frenchman had been wounded in the leg at Brandywine but since had returned to his troops. However, Gil had no luck in seeing the famed twenty-one-year-old Marquis on this trip to the Orderly Room.

Gil presented his commanding officer's strength report at the Adjutant General's desk. Then he sought the Quartermaster's office. The heat of the Headquarters building was terrific in comparison with the chill of the outside. Soon Gil was sweating and wanting to leave this warm place— something he had never dreamed he would want to do again. He was glad to see that the line he had joined was moving steadily past a harassed young clerk who wiped his pallid face from time to time and muttered some complaint.

As Gil stepped up to the desk the clerk's eyes rolled. His body went limp, and he fell off his stool to lie on the muddied floor. In falling he upset a small leaden ink bottle over a page of finely inscribed figures. A volley of plaintive wails broke out.

"Confound that stupid fool! I told him he should have gone on Sick Call this morning! Now he's ruined a whole page of accounts that took him a full day to draft! Find Amory!" The red-faced officer hammered his rude desk as he bellowed. "Take Cromwell to the kitchen and find Amory!"

"He's sick, too, sir," somebody answered. "We've four clerks down with the camp fever."

The Commissary Officer groaned and put his head down in his hands.

"What are we going to do?" he demanded of the world. "That report *must* go to Reading to-night!"

Gil stepped forward hesitantly.

"Sir, I ain't bad at figures, and I can write a fair hand."

"Then sit down at that desk, boy," said the Quartermaster, "and we'll see what you can do."

After Gil had copied the first five lines and had totted up a column of figures, the officer's expression relaxed.

"You'll do," he said. Now get to work on a copy of those figures Cromwell just baptized in ink. I'll have you ordered to detached duty here for a couple of days."

Thus it came about that Private Gil Weston worked in George Washington's Headquarters and saw many of the leading officers of the ragtag army on which rested the hopes of American liberty. He was set to adding up accounts and entering important letters into the General Headquarters Copy Book. And Gil never forgot one of these letters written by George Washington, the Commander-in-Chief, to one Henry Champion, Deputy Commissioner-General of Purchases.

"The present Situation of the Army is the most Melancholy that can be conceived. Our Supplies in provisions of the Flesh kind, for some Time past, have been very deficient and irregular, a Prospect now opens of absolute Want, such as will make it impossible to keep the Army much longer from dissolving, unless the most vigorous and effectual Measures be pursued to prevent it . . . If every possible Exertion is not made use of there, to send us immediate and ample Supplies of Cattle, with pain I speak the alarming Truth, no Human Efforts can keep the Army from speedily disbanding. . . ."

From this point of vantage Gil came to understand the army's truly desperate straits.

It was during the second week of Gil's detached duty that a farmer came clumping into Headquarters in clumsy cowhide boots. He was red-faced, blond-bearded and, from his speech, of Swedish origin. When Gil showed him in to Captain Stanhope, the duty officer that day in the Commissary-General's office, the Captain told him to stay and take notes.

"Farmer Matson," said the Captain, "is one of the most loyal Patriots in this area."

It developed that Farmer Matson had plenty to say in his deep, slow-spoken voice. He told Captain Stanhope that British agents had been busy in the farm lands during the past few days, offering purses filled with clinking gold pieces for meat and produce. The prices offered, Farmer Matson said, had been high enough to tempt all but the most loyal farmers.

The bearded man went on to explain that a rendezvous for wagons and carts of food bought from the farmers had been set near Pennypacker Mills. There, the carts would be taken in convoy by Major Simcoe's green-jacketed Queen's Rangers who would guard the train into Philadelphia.

However, on the way to the rendezvous the turncoat farmers must furnish their own protection. This was not a difficult task, actually, because the country thereabouts was liberally sprinkled with Tories.

"If only we had more cavalry!" groaned Captain Stanhope. "If we had half a troop of horses that could even walk, much less gallop, we could cut off some of those wagons before they reached the rendezvous."

"Please, Mister Matson," asked Gil, "when does all this take place?"

"In yust two days' time," replied the squat, blond-bearded fellow in the linsey-woolsey breeches and calfskin jacket. He blinked at the youngster behind the clerk's desk.

"Be quiet, Weston," Captain Stanhope snapped. "Nobody bade you speak."

A flush mounted to Gil's face, but he caught his breath and persisted.

"Your pardon, sir," he said. "But I've just remembered a trick played on the British near Machias, in Massachusetts, by Colonel Joe Gorham's men last year."

"Ya? Vot vass it?" asked Matson, interestedly. The thick-bodied Swede listened to Gil's story, scratching his head and staring at the gritty planked floor. Captain Stanhope arose, dangerously calm.

"That will do, m'lad," he grated. "Maybe you mean well, but what you propose is much too risky. No officer in his right mind would attempt anything like that. Suppose you return to your ink pot, Weston. Leave the fighting of this war to your Commander-in-Chief."

"Ya," said Farmer Matson, "but this boy——"

"——Is like all boys, full of vain imaginings," cut in Stanhope.

A few minutes later Farmer Matson emerged from Captain Stanhope's office. He was red in the face, and his pale blue eyes were sparkling with anger.

"Half a day I ride through the thick snow to come here," he grumbled. "And what is done? Nothings!"

A quick glance told Gil that the door to Captain Stanhope's office was closed. He slipped from behind his desk and tugged at the farmer's sleeve.

"Please, sir," he said in a low hurried voice, "would you wait for me a few minutes by the bake ovens across the road?"

The big farmer stared down at this slender boy in the buckskin breeches and greasy Indian leggings.

"I do not promise," he said. "It is a long vay home. But maybe I stop to light mine pipe."

In frantic haste, Gil drove his quill to complete the last entries in the Copy Book. He delivered the book to Captain Stanhope and was told that he had been relieved of his clerk's assignment. The ill man, Cromwell, had been proclaimed fit to return to his desk so Gil was ordered to report back to Wayne's Brigade and Captain Bartow. Gil saluted and half ran out of Headquarters. He saw with a bounding heart that Farmer Matson was waiting by a blackened bake oven. Although stacks of firewood were heaped all about the stove it was as cold as the others because there was nothing to bake.

"So?" rumbled the chunky, blue-clad farmer. "You do not give up so easy, like your Captain?"

"N-n-no, sir," Gil panted. "Please, sir, I think maybe I know of an officer who'd be interested in your story, Mister Matson."

During his service at Headquarters, Private Gil Weston had come to admire greatly that peppery, vigorous and resourceful Pennsylvania Militia General, James Potter. General Jim Potter was in command of the defenses on the far bank of the frozen Schuylkill River and the approaches from Philadelphia. Furthermore, Gil knew that Captain McLain's Oneida Indian Scouts had been attached to Potter's command only a short time before. It was to Potter's Brigade Headquarters therefore that the young New Englander now led the stolid Pennsylvanian.

General Potter had just returned from a tour of his outposts. He was sipping raspberry leaf tea when Gil and Farmer Matson reached the snug little cabin which was his headquarters. Gil and his chunky companion were immediately brought before the General. The big, brown-faced General paid close attention with his lively dark eyes as the boy outlined his plan.

"Will you furnish the necessary wagon and team?" General Potter asked the farmer when Gil was finished talking.

"Ya. I will do that."

The General's balding head turned as he crossed the room to load a corncob pipe from a box on the rough mantelpiece.

"I presume you realize, my friend," he warned, "that you stand an excellent chance of losing not only your property but also your life if this business goes wrong?"

The farmer nodded and his pale blue eyes blinked solemnly.

"Some Redcoats raided mine farm last fall," he explained slowly. "They took ten of mine cows and because I was no Tory they would not pay. I do not like the British since."

To the anxiously waiting Gil, General Potter said:

"I think it would only be fair for you to take part in your own scheme, even if you are a mite young. But you'll have to apply for special duty with my brigade. Do you think your Captain will agree to that?"

This was the question that Gil had been dreading. Captain Bartow's company was so fearfully under strength that there wasn't a chance in the world that that crusty old officer would even consider such a request. General Potter sensed Gil's confusion.

"Well, Weston," he smiled, "if that's the way it is, I guess what I don't know won't worry me."

He held a blazing pine shaving to the bowl of his corncob pipe. "But if you get into trouble over this I can't help you. Understand?"

"Yes, sir," Gil said quietly. "Now I'll just go fetch my Indian friend—though I ain't quite sure how well he and those Oneidas are going to get along."

10

Silent Death on the Pike

IT WAS A MID-FEBRUARY DAY WHEN THE TURN-coat farmers loaded their carts and headed them for the rendezvous near Pennypacker Mills. The day had dawned with a thaw which sent rivulets of melted snow coursing along the ruts of the Perkiomen Road. But after noon the temperature had dropped again.

An outpost on duty on the heights above the Schuylkill could have noticed a huge farm cart drawn by four horses plodding along, far to the north of the river. Another was advancing along a lane to the westward. Two more had just appeared from a northerly direction. Presently yet another wagon jolted along over the lane leading to Phoenixville.

Amidst a patch of snow-covered firs, a sixth cart waited. Two powerful, dappled gray draught horses stretched their necks to nibble at nearby birch twigs. On the driver's seat crouched a chunky, yellow-haired man in a rabbit's fur hat and a short brown cape. By his side sat a youth of some seventeen years who held a British cavalry carbine across his lap.

This weapon was unloaded. So were the muskets of Captain Joshua Hayden of Potter's Brigade and McDermott, a bandy-legged sergeant who waited on the other side of the cart. These two soldiers had donned countrymen's clothes, floppy brown, broad-brimmed felt hats and trousers of tow cloth stuffed into bulky cowhide boots. Hickory-dyed homespun shirts and long woolen mufflers completed their disguises. A stained brown tarpaulin had been rigged to cover the contents of the wagon body.

Their long wait stretched on until finally they were rewarded by the sound of voices, the cracking of whips and the snorting of horses that labored to pull their wagons along the slushy road. Captain Hayden's piercing black eyes darted inquiringly to Farmer Matson's watery blue ones. The Swede shook his head. Then he raised one flap of his fur cap and listened. After what seemed ages, the farmer calmly gathered his reins and clucked to his team. The powerful grays put weight into their collars. The wagon shuddered, the axles whined, and two men dressed as Tory guards shouldered their empty muskets.

The wagon jolted down a short hill and emerged onto the Pennypacker Mills Pike just after the preceding cart had disappeared around a bend. Farmer Matson hunched further over, bracing his body, praying silently.

When Matson's wagon came out onto the Pennypacker Mills Pike it was the sixth unit in a train of carts proceeding along the road. Like Matson's wagon, these other vehicles were under guard. Sometimes as many as four armed men tramped along beside the wheels that screeched toward the rendezvous at Pennypacker Mills.

Gil figured that night would fall within another hour. Perhaps by then eternal darkness would fall on several men now alive and hardy.

When the wagon ahead disappeared around a bend, Captain Hayden called over the creaking of axles.

"Reckon it's time to close up?"

"Ya," Matson nodded, and bent forward calling something in Swedish to his team. At once the powerful beasts moved forward at a quickened pace just short of a trot. The going soon became so rough that Gil had to hang on for dear life, the carbine jouncing in his lap. He didn't feel so happy about the weapon's being unloaded, but he understood the importance of keeping it empty.

They overtook the last cart just after the vehicle immediately ahead of it had disappeared around a tongue of hardwoods.

"Hi! One minute!" Matson called. "I got news for you!"

The driver ahead pulled up. The three Tory partisans doing escort duty halted and grounded their arms as they watched Matson's wagon approach. As the two grays came up on the Tory cart Captain Hayden and Sergeant McDermott made a pretense of tightening the tarpaulin. Actually they were releasing reef knots securing the canvas.

"Whoa!" Farmer Matson pulled his team to a steamy halt.

"Let's get busy!" Captain Hayden ordered in a low, tense voice.

The whole operation was smoothly executed. Matson and Gil leaped off the wagon seat into the snow and ran to steady the team by their bridles. From under the tarpaulin burst forth a dozen dark-skinned figures.

The other cart's driver and the three riflemen were frozen in their tracks by the paralysis of complete surprise. Then came the twang of bowstrings and the rushing hiss of flying death as the Oneidas sped arrows from their heavy war bows.

A dozen arrows streaked toward the enemy before they quite knew what was happening. All the Tories except the driver crumpled or struggled redly, silently, on the snow. Black feathered shafts protruded from the driver's thigh and shoulder. He made no outcry but started clumsily to run for a clump of pines.

He had almost reached shelter when Silver Hawk's war bow hummed. The Tory stumbled. His head snapped back and then he fell, a yellow feathered arrow quivering in the base of his neck.

It was a mighty pretty shot. Even the dour, dark-faced Oneidas grunted an approving "*Wagh!*"

The Indians, their scalping knives glinting blue-white, started fanning out purposefully but Captain Hayden snapped an order.

"None of that! No time for scalps. Pick up those Tory guns and heave 'em into the cart. Sergeant McDermott, you turn this wagon about and drive back along this road. Our people are waiting back at the crossroads."

The captured cart was turned and rumbled past. Gil caught a glimpse of barrels of flour, sides of bacon, carcasses of pork and beef. Well he knew what they would mean to the wretches shivering in those huts beyond the Schuylkill. This thought did much to dispel the horror of that lightning, merciless attack on men content to watch their countrymen starve while they pocketed British gold.

Hayden, who looked like an Indian himself be-

Then came the twang of Indian bowstrings.

cause of his beaked face, straight black hair and small, glittering dark eyes, began to roar in Iroquois, "Back to the wagon! Quickly! Quickly! Those carts up ahead still have to be taken!"

The Oneidas obeyed only reluctantly, disappointed at losing the scalps. Silver Hawk, though, scrambled up into the wagon's body as nimbly as a squirrel; the other Indians followed. The tarpaulin was secured again, and Matson whipped up the grays.

The next cart they overtook had stopped, and its driver and guards were working on a broken trace. There was no need to kill anybody this time. When the Tory farmers saw the Indians descend upon them they dropped their guns, raised their hands and begged for mercy. This cart also was turned about and started back along the pike. Its ex-owner and Tory escorts, gagged and bound, were left by the highway, as helpless as calves tied up for sticking.

There was trouble, however, when the third cart

was overtaken. It was just below the brow of a hill that hid it from the leading two vehicles. A little dark-browed Welsh farmer managed to fire a shot from his blunderbuss before he died with an Oneida arrow through his throat. The explosion reverberated between a series of low ridges, sounding like some giant's bowling ball.

"Back into the wagon!" rasped Hayden. "The shot may not have been heard—or those up ahead may not pay much attention to a single shot." He turned to Gil. "Son, you'd better take this wagon in."

"Yes, sir," Gil said obediently. His heart sagged with disappointment at being ordered back before this adventure he had set in motion was finished. He climbed onto the third wagon's seat, downcast. Silver Hawk paused to wave his bow.

"Farewell, *Muen*, my brother," the Micmac called. "We feast on fat meat tomorrow!"

The young Indian had turned to follow Matson's cart when Gil saw one of the fallen wagon guards raise his head. Then as he saw Gil's eyes upon him the Tory jumped up and started to run. Silver Hawk whirled in his tracks, swift as a ferret, and took out after the man.

Gil Weston watched Silver Hawk put on a desperate burst of speed, saw the Micmac snatch a slender war hatchet from his belt as he ran. Gil saw his arm sweep back then swing forward, stopping short in mid-arc. The throwing axe spun over and over until it struck the runner just below the neck. The Tory flung out his arms and fell. It seemed as if he were trying to clasp a clump of snow-covered huckleberry bushes to his breast as his long legs threshed about—and he lay still.

Silver Hawk waved again at Gil. He paused only long enough to retrieve his axe then pelted off after Farmer Matson's team.

11

Trouble in Camp

IT WAS THE DEAD OF NIGHT WHEN THE FIRST OF the captured carts entered Valley Forge. Yet when the magic word "food" was heard a detail of General Washington's Bodyguards turned out, and the glad news was flashed through the encampment. A rush was made at the first three food-laden wagons but the Bodyguards beat it off without trouble.

Torches flared in the darkness as General

Greene's personal aide appeared. He ordered the captured food to be placed under heavy guard, and the wagons creaked on to the Commissary-General's empty barns.

"Never could a prize be more welcome," rumbled the Commissary-Colonel. "General Greene extends his compliments to General Potter and Captain Hayden."

"There'll be two more wagons along soon, sir," said Sergeant McDermott. "They'd be here now except we had a little fight with Simcoe's Green Jackets and had to run 'em halfway to Philadelphia."

Gil was squatting on his heels beside a campfire on which a portion of the booty was being cooked when a hand closed on his collar and jerked him to his feet.

"So there yez are, ye tricky little spalpeen!" Corporal Cassidy roared. "We'll see what Cap'n Bartow's got in store for yez, ye sneakin' pup of a deserter!"

Dazedly, Gil staggered along, pricked now and then by the point of Cassidy's bayonet. He still had not found his voice when he stood before the scowling Captain Bartow.

"I found one of these runaway whelps, sir," reported the Corporal. "He was over by the Commissary, settin' by the fire and stuffin' hisself, as brash as ye please."

"But, sir, I—"

"Silence!" thundered Bartow. His heavy features turned brick red. "I'll hear nothing from you, you puppy, except the yelps you'll raise when you feel thirty lashes well laid on! You and that savage, when I lay hands on him!"

"Oh, no!" Gil gasped. "Please listen! We've done nothing wrong, sir!"

"Take him away!" roared the company commander.

In later years, Gil could recall little of his journey to the guard house. There he was thrown in among thieves, drunkards, deserters and other vil-

lains, all suffering in a stinking, icy hovel. His chief worry, when he was able to think clearly, was the need to warn Silver Hawk. He realized in despair that this was almost an impossibility.

Somehow the night crawled by. To the young prisoner's ears came the familiar music of fifes and drums playing the reveille. Uksene-ak had not been brought to the guard house. Could he have been warned? There were many men of Wayne's Brigade who owed their lives to the Micmac's skill in foraging. They might have told him what lay in store for him here at camp.

Or he might have been wounded, or even

killed, in the skirmish after Gil had turned back with the captured cart. Fervently, Gil prayed that Silver Hawk might have suffered a light wound— just bad enough to keep him out of Captain Bartow's vengeful hands until Captain Hayden's voice could be heard.

Now his fellow prisoners began to wake. One after the other they were summoned to the guard room where they would have their wrists tied and would then be marched away to their respective units. A muffled moan escaped the boy when the Sergeant of the Guard sang out: "Private Gilbert Weston, report here!"

Three muskets had been lashed together to form a tripod. Beside it stood little Billy Watson who, though only twelve years of age, could drum as well as the next man. Billy looked miserable. Gil had often befriended the lad.

Captain Bartow stepped out of his hut as the Fourth Company drew up in a double rank.

" 'Tis an outrage," Gil heard one tall, black-haired man mutter. "After all him and his Injun friend done fer this Company you'd think—"

"Silence!" barked a lieutenant. "Silence, else you'll get a taste of the same. Now listen to orders."

The lieutenant unrolled a scrap of grimy paper and read aloud:

"For absenting himself from duty with his Company without permission, Private Gilbert Weston of the Third Squad is hereby sentenced to suffer thirty strokes of the lash well laid on his bare back. By order of Captain Bartow!"

Corporal Cassidy strode forward and gripped Gil's shoulders.

"Step up to the tripod, Bub," he growled.

Gil glared about him wildly. His heart sickened at the thought of this brutal indignity, of the horrible, unmerited disgrace that was about to be dealt him. An overwhelming impulse to break free and run seized him. It was no use. His hands had been tightly lashed together.

Now a corporal stood fingering a long thong attached to a wooden handle. He had been assigned from another company lest he be tempted to lay on the whip too lightly. He seemed the type of man who would relish a job like this.

"No!" Gil screamed. "This ain't fair! Sure I absented myself but it was to capture food! Food for you and the whole army."

"Corporal, do your duty!" snapped the Captain.

A new voice that sounded vaguely familiar broke in.

"Just what is going on here, Captain?"

Gil wrenched his head around. There was a group of horsemen reining in behind Captain Bartow. The leading rider was broad-shouldered and cool-eyed. Now he spoke again as Bartow goggled.

"This man says he captured food, Captain. Is he being whipped for that?"

Recognition came then to Gil's tear-filled eyes.

"General Greene, please, sir!" he called. "Don't let them whip me!"

"Odd's blood!" came a voice from behind General Greene. Captain Stanhope spurred forward. "It's young Weston, the clerk!" He turned in his saddle and saluted the General.

"Sir, this is the young fellow who first suggested the plan by which General Potter's men captured some Tory supply wagons yesterday."

General Greene leaned forward in his saddle, soothing his restless back.

"So?" he asked, quietly. Then his voice sharpened. "You!" he flung at Cassidy. "Untie that man's hands. And you, Private Weston, report to General Headquarters."

"But, sir—" Captain Bartow objected.

"My orders," Greene rapped out and turned his big stallion away.

It was close to noon that day when Gil Weston found his friend, Silver Hawk. He was in that scene of dreadful suffering, the bleak barn which served as the Valley Forge Flying Hospital.

The Micmac was not seriously wounded. He

134

wore his left arm in a sling but otherwise appeared unharmed. After the two friends left the charnel house with its shrieks and moans, Uksene-ak explained.

"It is nothing," he told Gil. "A bullet grazed my shoulder. The white medicine men poured rum and water into the wound, and that was all." He looked back at the house of pain and shuddered. "Let us be away from here."

"What happened after I turned back with my wagon?" Gil asked.

"There was a little fight in a small valley when we overtook the lead cart," the Micmac said. "Some Rangers were waiting for us at a crossroads behind a ridge. They had heard that blunderbuss, you remember? We were just taking the first wagon when they attacked."

"What happened then, Uksene-ak?"

"The Oneidas," Silver Hawk replied grudgingly, "fought well—for Iroquois. Two of them were killed by the green-coated horsemen but in the first attack four of the Tories were sent by our arrows to hunt in the Land Beyond the Rising Sun. When two more of the enemy fell, they turned their horses and fled. Tell me, *Muen*, my brother, why do we follow this path? It does not lead to our hut."

"And it won't ever, Hawk."

Briefly Gil told his Indian friend what had happened since he had last seen him. He recounted the story of his treatment by Corporal Cassidy and Captain Bartow and of General Greene's lucky intervention.

"So," he wound up, "thanks to General Greene and Captain Stanhope, we have been transferred to General Potter's Frontier Militia."

A quick smile lit the young Indian's face.

"*Wagh!*" he said. "That is good!"

12
"Paddy"

THE MORNING OF THE SEVENTEENTH OF MARCH, 1778, dawned clear and bright. This was a cheerful omen to the wild Irishmen of Morgan's Virginia Riflemen and to the Scotch-Irish soldiers from Virginia, Georgia and the Carolinas.

Gil was filling a kettle at Dewees' Spring when an outraged clamor arose from the direction of Dan Morgan's Brigade of Virginia Riflemen. The noise grew so loud that Potter's troops dropped what they were doing and started running through the encampment toward the Virginia cantonments.

Gil saw a mob of furious Irishmen in hunting shirts and long buckskins, milling about and shaking their fists in the air. The greasy fringe on their shirts rippled with their wrath.

High on an exposed limb of a huge white oak dangled a grotesque effigy wearing a halo of twisted rope. On the dummy's chest was a large square of paper. Upon it, the word "Paddy" had been written in bold black letters.

"Dishonor the good Saint, will they?" stormed the Irishmen. "We'll make somebody pay for this. And on St. Patrick's own day, too—'tis a rare insult!"

"Who was it?" they clamored. "Did anybody see who done it?"

"A-hah!" A tall, black-haired Irishman leveled his forefinger at the dangling effigy. "Look! That's German writin' on yon sign. This is the doin' of them Pennsylvania Dutchmen, I'll be bound!"

More and more red-faced Irishmen were gathering, and the crowd's voice took on an ugly tone.

"Aye. Sure as shootin', 'twas those no-good Dutchmen of the First Pennsylvania," somebody yelled. "Come on, boys! Let's go get 'em!"

Terrible were the threats of the infuriated Irishmen as they started across the Grand Parade. As

139

luck would have it, they came across a company of Lieutenant-Colonel Wetner's troops at drill. The Pennsylvania Dutchmen seemed to be having trouble hiding their snickers as they went through their squads-right and squads-left.

"*Nein!* Don't shoot!" bellowed a huge sergeant. "It vass not us! It vass der Bluenoses—der Yankee men!"

Quickly the angry mob of Morgan's men was swelled by everyone in camp who was a son of St. Patrick—or fancied himself one—or who just felt in need of a good brawl. A slow and ominous movement started toward that section of the encampment occupied by the New England brigades.

The situation appeared to be rapidly getting out of hand. General Potter stormed through the camp bareheaded. With sword in hand he roared at his men to go back to their tasks. But his shouted threats went for naught. Everywhere men were catching up muskets, slinging their ammunition pouches and fixing their bayonets in place. It looked as though a general riot was in the making.

The tumult swelled louder as Morgan's leather-faced riflemen started up the slope toward the New Englanders. Nothing on earth, it seemed, could prevent a murderous clash.

Suddenly drums began beating in the cantonment occupied by Washington's Bodyguards, close to General Headquarters. Two neatly-uniformed platoons of Bodyguards appeared on the double. At the sight of those long muskets topped by fixed bayonets most of the would-be rioters slowed their rush to a walk. Then followed the hollow clatter of a troop of horses moving at a brisk trot.

From the direction of General Headquarters rode a figure that was immediately recognized by everybody. A cheer broke out here, another there. Soon the huzzas of the men who would have been at each other's throats were blended in a continuous roar.

Riding with superb ease, General Washington

spurred his handsome gray stallion toward the center of trouble. Behind him rode red-headed General de Lafayette, burly General Greene and the gaudily-uniformed Pole, Count Casimir Pulaski.

As deliberately as though he were reviewing a parade, General Washington reined in. His quiet gaze swept the hot and angry red faces about him.

"Men," he said, in a deep grave voice, "I am delighted to find so many of you here. I am in a mood to celebrate." A grim smile tugged at the corners of his wide mouth as he continued. "This day is the second anniversary of the British evacuation of Boston. It is also St. Patrick's Day and I, too, am a lover of St. Patrick. Therefore, I am ordering the whole army to take a holiday until reveille, tomorrow."

Never had Valley Forge resounded to such a tremendous cheer as the one that then arose. Forgotten were the threats that had been passed between the Irishmen and the New Englanders. The

Yankees swore their complete innocence in the affair of "Paddy." So did the Pennsylvanians— who were really the guilty parties. Since the trouble-making effigy had long since been cut down there seemed to be small point in keeping the quarrel alive. So arms were stacked, and the troops began a round of visiting each other's cantonments. Fraternization became the order of the day.

Once again, George Washington had by his mere presence saved a situation that could have resulted in bloodshed and violence.

13
Tarleton's Dragoons

A MARCH THAW RAISED HIGH THE HOPES OF THE men at Valley Forge. They looked forward to spring and a run of shad up the Schuylkill which would end the food problem. They spoke eagerly of breaking out of winter quarters to attack the British.

But winter came back with a vengeance. Yet again icy blizzards howled over Mount Joy and Mount Misery. Yet once more the Schuylkill froze

over so solidly that artillery and heavy wagons
could move across the ice. Again the snow drifted
down. Again the men of George Washington's
Army suffered from hunger.

Reports from Patriots in Philadelphia said that
"Dandy Sir Billy" Howe was finally bestirring
himself. He was tearing himself away from the
round of parties given him by Tories there and
making ready for a spring campaign. It was ex-
pected that this campaign would be preceded by
some sort of move, probably a raid in force,
against the Continental Army.

With the Schuylkill River and other streams
frozen solid, there was no need of fording. A
British attack on Valley Forge became possible
from several directions. None was more alive to
the danger of the situation than General George
Washington. Because he still lacked any strong
force of scouts, he knew the enemy could surprise
him from almost any direction. The Commander-
in-Chief, therefore, ordered a wide semicircle of

observation posts set in tall trees about Valley Forge. Strong outposts were established at strategic points.

The Oneidas, under Captain McLain, were sent off to guard the Bethlehem-Skipjack Road. General Potter's frontiersmen were ordered to protect the Valley Forge approaches. These troops were stationed among ravines and roads winding toward the winter encampment.

There followed several sharp brushes with the hit-and-run Queen's Rangers commanded by Major J. G. Simcoe. Those green-jacketed Tories more than once swooped down on an unwary outpost and dashed off again, leaving a scattering of bodies behind. It was generally said that the lucky ones were those who were killed in these raids. A worse fate was to be dragged off to the Market Prison at Philadelphia where the brutal Provost William Cunningham held sway. Cunningham had been a "scaw-broker," or kidnaper of child labor, before he was appointed as prison keeper. His cruel tactics at Market Prison sickened even his fellow officers.

There was another troop of Redcoat raiders, new to the area. These dragoons were under the command of the hated Major Banastre Tarleton. It was said of Tarleton that ice water, not blood, ran in his veins.

The temperatures this bitter winter never had been lower than during the first week in April. Even Gil Weston bemoaned the fact that he and Silver Hawk had been assigned to a Valley Forge approaches outpost.

A late storm was coating Pennsylvania with a layer of silvery powder and the flakes came down furiously. They whirled through the naked brown-black branches of a big sentinel oak in which Gil had been shivering for nearly three hours. It was a welcome sight to see his relief come toiling up the ladder to a hogshead fixed among the oak's branches as a makeshift observation post.

As he trudged toward the outpost barracks, a

well-plundered two-story farmhouse near Signal Hill, Gil recalled that there was going to be a modest party at camp this evening. The outpost's commanding officer, a pleasant, soft-spoken man named Captain Henry Lee, was going to celebrate his twenty-second birthday with the help of the fourteen men constituting his guard detachment. Future generations would know and forever honor the name of Captain Henry Lee's still unborn son. He would be Robert E. Lee, hero of the Confederate States of America.

When Gil arrived a huge fire was roaring in the wide fireplace of the partially rebuilt old farmhouse. Several rabbits caught by Silver Hawk were broiling on a spit, together with a sizable shoulder of pork.

Most of the soldiers sat on the floor. They ate from chestnut burl bowls which, along with their hickory twig forks and pocket knives, made up their mess equipment.

Soon a Maryland soldier raised his voice in one of the more popular songs of the day:

> *Come, join hand-in-hand*
> *Brave Americans all;*
> *And rouse your whole band*
> *At Liberty's call.*

A Virginia soldier then produced a sack of black walnuts. These were handed around to have their shells cracked by pistol butts, faggots and stones from the rude fireplace fender. All in all it became a very pleasant affair and festivities were running high. Suddenly Silver Hawk left the convivial semi-circle before the fireplace. He trotted to one of the blanket-draped windows and peered out into the gathering gloom. He muttered an exclamation, whirled and called back to Captain Lee.

"Horses, Captain! Many horses and very near!"

The men scrambled for their muskets, pistols and pikes. A ragged volley rang out from the eastern end of the shallow hollow containing this old Welsh farmhouse. Gil buttoned his coat and slipped the slings of his powder horn and bullet bag over his shoulder. Then he crouched below a window sill and peered out into the darkening farmyard.

"British dragoons, Captain!" somebody cried softly. "It looks like they have us surrounded!"

A militiaman burst in through the front door a moment before the heavy oaken bars were slammed into place.

"They're all around us, sir!" he panted. "By grabs, the woods is full of 'em. Must be a couple of hundred Lobsterbacks."

"Two men to each window!" Captain Lee's young voice rang out clearly and calmly. "One to fire while the other reloads. Hold your fire till you get a sure target."

Gil could hear men moving about upstairs. They were the marksmen Captain Lee had detailed as snipers whose special targets were to be the enemy officers.

"You get up there, too!" the Virginian told Silver Hawk. "They can use those sharp eyes of yours up there!"

Gil squinted through a torn hole in the blanket. There was not too much daylight left, he realized. A golden sun ray suddenly broke through the storm clouds to show seven horsemen galloping up. They were lurching along a path which had been made by some farmer's cows in the past.

"There they be!" a soldier yelled. The farmhouse thundered to an explosion that briefly lighted the room with a flash of fire from the muskets' pans.

British voices rang outside.

"Surrender, ye Rebel dogs! Surrender, or die!"

They were dragoons, all right, Gil told himself. They wore high black jackboots, scarlet shell jackets and black-plumed brass helmets. Now they spurred forward, bending low over their horses' necks with their pistols held out in front of them. Not five yards from the stone farmhouse they leveled their weapons and fired. The men at the windows inside answered. Dense clouds of smoke rolled up, blotting out everything.

The British kept riding up to the windows, firing, and then spurring away to reload their horse pistols. Shots hissed through the windows, knocking big chunks of plaster from the scarred ceiling and walls. Two of the blankets covering the farmhouse windows caught fire and smouldered, filling the room with the stench of burning wool.

Captain Lee stalked over to a window behind which a soldier had been hit. Straddling the wounded man, the Virginian twitched aside the blanket and fired quickly. There followed a hoarse scream. Then came the sound of more dragoons charging up to the attack.

The racket became so deafening that Gil's head swam and his eardrums ached. All the same, he sensed that shots were being exchanged on the other side of the farmhouse. The riflemen on the upper floor were pouring bullet after bullet into the attackers. How was Silver Hawk making out upstairs? All right, probably, because the men up there were better protected than those on the ground floor. Upstairs, the enemy could aim at only the half-windows, built under the low eaves.

Still the assault gained weight until the whole snow-covered farmyard was filled by a weird pattern of swirling horses and riders. A few dragoons dismounted and commenced a furious battering on the front door with the butts of their carbines.

A high-pitched voice—the voice of Tarleton—cried out:

"Surrender now, ye blasted Rebels! Surrender or we'll burn you out!"

There was a lull in the firing. Captain Lee's voice sounded clearly over the stamping of the horses and the champing of their bits.

"Stone houses are hard to burn. Come on again, sir! And a very hearty welcome to you from our guns!"

14

Two Sergeants

DISMOUNTED THIS TIME, THE BIG BRITISH DRA-
goons hurled still another attack at the farmhouse.
They advanced right up to the windows and
fired their short carbines into the rooms. Two
Americans were killed, and a yelling dragoon corporal actually threw his leg across one of the window sills before Captain Lee saved the day. The
young Virginian hammered at the Britisher with
the butt of his horse pistol and stunned him,

155

knocking him back into the yard with a blow in the face.

Gil's carbine was empty. He was reloading it when he saw another saber-swinging dragoon lean far through a window, slashing at a wounded militiaman. Gil reversed his gun to use it as a club and then leaped for the Redcoat. The dragoon aimed a whistling cut at the boy's head which Gil partially parried. The saber blade glanced off, but not widely enough. Gil took a deep gash in his left shoulder. Stricken by a paralyzing pain, he reeled back while his carbine clattered to the floor. Biting back his groans, he managed to pick up the gun and throw it one-handed. The carbine struck the scarlet-and-white figure full in the chest. The dragoon fell backward, howling.

Again the British were driven off, leaving more motionless bodies scattered about the farmyard. Hurriedly the little garrison reloaded. But this time a fearful undertone spread as man after man shook his powder horn.

"Runnin' mighty low!"

"We'll be out of powder in a few more rounds!"

His head ringing with the report of muskets, Gil stood in a corner and stared weakly at his left sleeve. Faintness quavered through his body. His whole sleeve was sodden and warm blood trickled down over his fingers. In clumsy fashion he tried to rig his neckerchief as a bandage, but it was dripping wet before he could tie it.

Captain Lee pulled aside a blanket to look out into the farmyard. Then he turned to face his men.

"Boys," he said, "I don't really know whether we'll be able to drive them off again. But"—his jaw tightened—"I don't aim to surrender. If any of you want to go out and give yourselves up, I grant you permission."

Nobody moved.

"Reckon we'll stay along with you, sir," grunted a grizzled old Marylander.

Lee turned as Silver Hawk came padding down the shaky stairs. The young Indian was covered with dust, and his high-boned features were streaked with burnt powder.

"Captain," he said softly, "Uksene-ak saw where Redcoats are. Dark is here soon and a ground fog begins to form. I, Silver Hawk, can get away and run for help from the next post."

"Nonsense!" snapped the handsome young Virginian. "You wouldn't have a chance. You'd have at least fifty yards of open ground to cover before you'd reach the woods. The enemy is mounted. They'd cut you down in a matter of seconds!"

Captain Lee frowned, resetting that screw which secured his pistol's flint.

"It's almost certain death," he pointed out. "But if we don't get help soon this outpost is surely done for."

Black eyes shining, the young Indian hurried over to where Gil was having his shoulder bandaged by another man. A piece of somebody's shirt served for cloth.

"*Muen,* my brother, if Uksene-ak does not return, tell Kitpoo, the Sachem of our people at Kespoogwit, that his grandson tried to fight as he would have him."

"You'll get through," Gil said. "You've *got* to get through!"

Pressed close to bullet-splintered window frames, the beleaguered outpost anxiously watched the Micmac's slender figure wriggle through a small cellar window. Silver Hawk crouched and made ready for that risky dash for the woods.

"Shoot!" Captain Lee called to the soldiers on the opposite side of the house. "Distract the Britishers' attention as much as you can."

The muskets boomed again, sending more billows of smoke whirling from their muzzles. From a window Gil watched his friend rise suddenly and bound across the stable yard. As easily as a young buck deer he hurdled a trooper's fallen horse and ducked under the wellsweep. He was halfway to safety before the first startled yells broke out from the enemy. Bent low, the Micmac dodged in zigzag leaps. He streaked over a log pile and a stone fence.

His goal was an evergreen copse that protruded like a tongue from the encircling woods. Again and again the British carbines cracked. Tarleton's lieutenants screeched commands. In agony, Gil saw a twig on a level with the Micmac's shoulder snapped off by a bullet. But his friend kept on.

Then a single report—a rifle's sharp bark—rang out. Silver Hawk lurched, stumbled, recovered and dodged into the woods just as the first mounted men spurred after him. Three red-jacketed dragoons urged their horses in furious pursuit as the young Indian became lost to sight.

"They'll cut him down for sure," sighed a gray-haired corporal. "Them woods ain't thick enough to shelter him."

There was no chance to watch the chase further.
Major Banastre Tarleton himself led nearly a hundred dragoons in a determined assault on foot
against the stone house. Raising a cheer, the British ran out of the woods, firing as they advanced.

Again the farmhouse windows spouted flame
and smoke, but the scarlet and the gold braid of

the dragoons gleamed close. Tarleton's dark, hatchet face peered inside. An American whipped up his musket and pulled the trigger. There was no flash, no shot. A misfire.

Tarleton's white teeth shone briefly.

"You missed me that time, m'lad," he said, quite calmly. Then he shot the unlucky American through the head and vanished from sight.

For a fourth time the British struggled to sweep into the house. For a fourth time their losses forced them to draw off.

"How's our powder holding out?" Captain Lee asked.

"This here's me last charge, sir."

"I'm plumb out."

"I got mebbe two more charges."

"In that case," the Virginian said, shaking his head, "we're in for it if they rush us again."

Gil, back at a window, studied the shifting mass of red-coated figures. They moved back and forth, out of range, beyond a grove of ancient oaks. Was there something new in the way they carried themselves? Was there something uncertain in the manner in which the British officers were handling their men? Had four costly rebuffs of a tiny outpost detachment of "Rebel dogs" done something to the vast and arrogant self-confidence of the King's dragoons?

"Look," Gil said suddenly. "There's no use just waiting for them to come at us again. Maybe we can fool 'em. Let's make out we see reinforcements comin'. Let's all yell as loud as we can."

"No harm tryin'," said a Virginian who held a tourniquet twisted tight above a gaping wound in his knee. "You just say the word."

Gil strained his eyes to watch Major Tarleton's spare, erect figure direct his troops into position for another charge.

"Now's the time!" Gil yelled. "There they come! Huzza! Huzza! Come on, you Rhode Islanders! Huzza! Go 'round to the right!"

The men around Gil raised such a clamor that

others in the farmhouse joined in, as wholly deceived as were the Britishers.

"Here they come!" they yipped. "Here come our boys!"

Gil watched Major Tarleton straighten and turn his head to peer over a big golden epaulet.

"Hurry, lads!" Lee cried at the top of his voice. "Hurry or the Lobsterbacks will get away! Huzza! Huzza!"

The line of British skirmishers had halted. The Redcoats were looking about wildly. Three or four of them abruptly turned and ran to the rear. Cursing, Major Tarleton hesitated an instant. Then he wheeled, shouting commands that sent his men pelting back to their horses. The British obviously feared they would be caught afoot by the "reinforcements" about to relieve the Americans.

As if to end the enemy's indecision, Captain Lee ordered his men to fire the last of their ammunition. The young Virginian's gamble paid off. The dragoons flung themselves into their saddles and galloped out of sight beyond a ridge and headed back to Philadelphia.

Whether the British commander was planning an ambush or not wasn't learned until a half hour later when two troops of Pulaski's Light Dragoons arrived. The American cavalrymen found nothing beyond the ridge. Tarleton's force had disappeared, leaving their dead behind them.

Captain Lee, returning to the farmhouse, looked about the shambles that had been the outpost headquarters.

"Who thought of raising that cheer?" he demanded tensely.

"Young Weston, sir," said the Virginian who wore a torniquet about his leg.

Lee walked over to where Gilbert Weston lay slumped against the wall. A rivulet of blood crept out from under his leggings.

"Fetch bandages, somebody!" the Captain ordered sharply. He bent over Gil's slight figure. "He's unconscious!"

"No, sir, I ain't." The youth's eyelids fluttered. "So Silver Hawk *did* get through!"

"Aye," said Lee softly. "He got through. And now just you lie still, Sergeant."

"Sergeant, sir?"

"Aye. You'll be Sergeant Weston from now on."

In the Flying Hospital confusion reigned. Overworked orderlies sped about putting things as straight as they could in the brief time they had before an unscheduled visit by the Commander-in-Chief himself.

When he appeared, General Washington was wearing a long, dark blue cloak that was weather-beaten about the shoulders and frayed at the hem. But his uniform bearing the buff revers of Virginia was spotless, and his buttons gleamed like stars.

Those among the patients who were strong enough raised a cheer. Somehow, even in the darkest days of Valley Forge, the sight of George

Washington's straight, tall figure was enough to bring a heartfelt cheer.

Accompanying the Commander-in-Chief was the Marquis de Lafayette. He looked not a day older than his twenty-one years. Smiling, charming and able, Lafayette was ranked by many as second only to Washington in the conduct of the Revolution.

Dr. Bodo Otto of the Medical Service hurried forward, pulling a tunic over his operating apron. He saluted and received Washington's return salute.

"The soldier you wish to see, Your Excellency, is unable to leave his pallet," the doctor said. "He has taken a bullet through the side, sir."

"Then most certainly," said General Washington, quietly, "we shall go to him."

The Micmac, Silver Hawk, lay sound asleep, his dark head looking very small upon a folded blanket. When Dr. Bodo Otto would have wakened him Washington held up a restraining hand.

From an aide he took a knot of green worsted such as sergeants wore on their right shoulders as their badge of rank.

"I trust, Doctor," Washington murmured, "that you will accord this soldier the very best of attention. I should deplore the loss of the newest sergeant in my Bodyguard."

15

Out of the Valley

THAT BRUSH WITH TARLETON'S MEN AND THE
rout of his dreaded dragoons by a handful of
patriots seemed to be the signal for a sharp change
in fortune. Spring—long overdue spring—came to
Valley Forge.

The Schuylkill ran thick with shad. Every man
could eat his fill for the first time in that winter
encampment's history. British supply line raiders
met with little success during April when the

weather should have been to their advantage. And they failed miserably in their attempts to seize wagon trains that began trickling in from Reading and Lancaster during early May.

General "Mad Anthony" Wayne roused from his gloomy torpor. He beseiged Headquarters with appeals for action until he received Washington's consent to forage among certain well-stocked Tory farms. Wayne boasted that he would seize seven thousand head of cattle and eighteen thousand barrels of flour. He did not do that well but he captured enough to earn himself the nickname of "Wayne the Drover."

And the killing cold retreated with enemy pressure on the outposts of Valley Forge. The men had lived through times that any military expert alive would swear would crush the morale of any army. They had weakened. They had faltered. They had lost all but the last shreds of hope. In the end they won their greatest victory of the War for Independence.

"Dandy Sir Billy" Howe was gone as British Commander-in-Chief. In his place was Sir Henry Clinton. To Clinton came reports that the plans Howe had made for an all-out assault on a disorganized, mutinous, hunger-wracked remnant of Washington's Army at Valley Forge were now so much waste paper.

"These Rebels," Clinton advised the Cabinet in London, "are thrice as strong now as when they were left to their doom at Valley Forge. What manner of men are these?"

Clinton decided that Philadelphia was no place for him. He gave his orders to prepare an evacuation of the city. He planned to march to Sandy Hook and there board ship for New York. Clinton was resigned to a return to the "stalemate war" that had existed before Howe had sailed to the Chesapeake in his brother's armada nearly a year before. Washington drew up his own plans.

On June 19, 1778, the British began withdrawing from Philadelphia. On that same day the first

detachments of Washington's Army marched out of Valley Forge in pursuit of the Redcoats.

Behind them they left the rude shacks, the un-marked graves, the fortifications that never had come under fire. They left the storehouses that had never been used until the last days of the encampment. They left the hospital where so many men had died and so many others had prayed for death. They left the whitened bones of starved

172

horses and the stumps of trees hacked down for precious firewood. They left the hard-packed parade ground where General von Steuben had made soldiers out of farmers. They left behind Valley Forge where the cause of Liberty was supposed to have been frozen, beaten and starved to death.

All this they and George Washington left behind them.

The Army sang smartly as its ordered regiments marched out of Valley Forge. Well it might. For all that, ahead of the men lay the bitter struggles of Monmouth, Stony Point, Ninety-Six, King's Mountain, Cowpens, Guilford Courthouse and Yorktown.

Ahead also lay victory and freedom!

Index